Popping with Power

Principal Authors
Ann Wiebe
Betty Cordel
Dave Youngs

Contributing Authors
Johanna Tomik

The Original Writing Team

Carol Bland	Sean Greene	Anne Rudig
Helen Crossley	Loretta Hill	Gina Wiens
Susan Dixon	Helen Rayfield	Nancy Williams

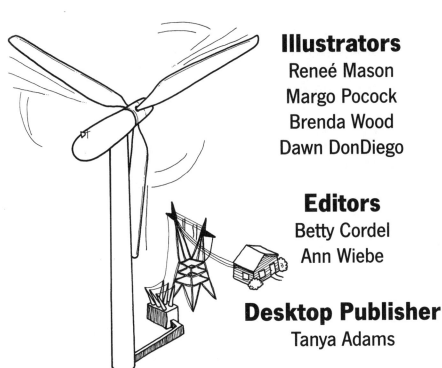

Illustrators
Reneé Mason
Margo Pocock
Brenda Wood
Dawn DonDiego

Editors
Betty Cordel
Ann Wiebe

Desktop Publisher
Tanya Adams

This book contains materials developed by the AIMS Education Foundation. **AIMS** (**A**ctivities **I**ntegrating **M**athematics and **S**cience) began in 1981 with a grant from the National Science Foundation. The non-profit AIMS Education Foundation publishes hands-on instructional materials (books and the quarterly magazine) that integrate curricular disciplines such as mathematics, science, language arts, and social studies. The Foundation sponsors a national program of professional development through which educators may gain both an understanding of the AIMS philosophy and expertise in teaching by integrated, hands-on methods.

• P.O. Box 8120, Fresno, CA 93747-8120 •
• 888.733.2467 • 559.255.6396 (fax) • aimsed@aimsedu.org •

ISBN: 978-1-932093-05-6

Printed in the United States of America

Table of Contents

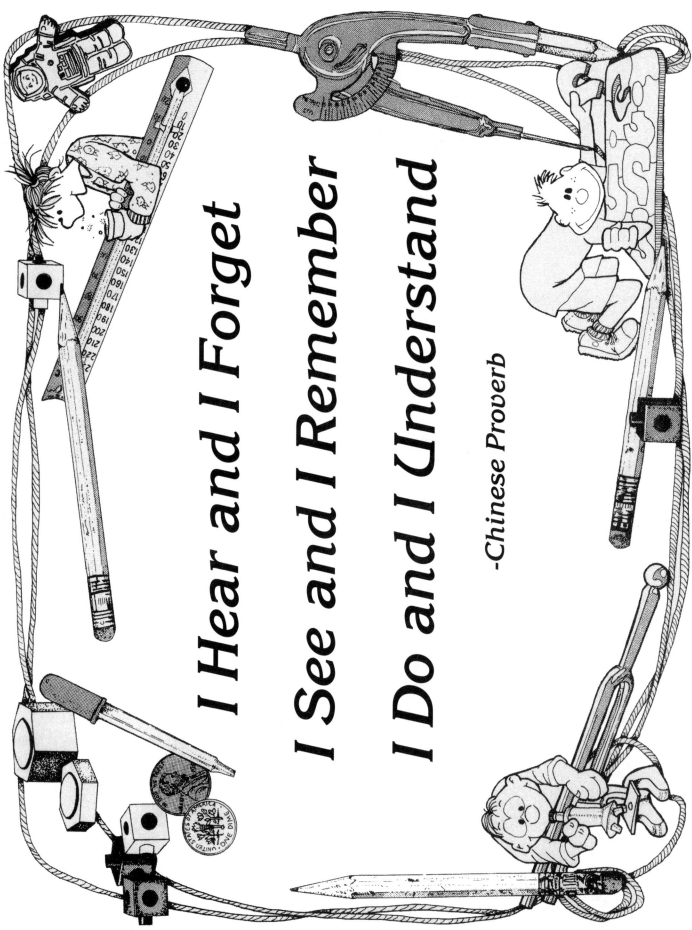

I Hear and I Forget

I See and I Remember

I Do and I Understand

-*Chinese Proverb*

National Reform Documents

The Nature of Science

- Results of scientific investigations are seldom exactly the same, but if the differences are large, it is important to try to figure out why. One reason for following directions carefully and for keeping records of one's work is to provide information on what might have caused the differences.
- Scientists' explanations about what happens in the world come partly from what they observe, partly from what they think. Sometimes scientists have different explanations for the same set of observations. That usually leads to their making more observations to resolve the differences.
- People can often learn about things around them by just observing those things carefully, but sometimes they can learn more by doing something to the things and noting what happens.

The Nature of Mathematics

- Mathematics is the study of many kinds of patterns, including numbers and shapes and operations on them. Sometimes patterns are studied because they help to explain how the world works or how to solve practical problems, sometimes because they are interesting in themselves.
- Mathematical ideas can be represented concretely, graphically, and symbolically.

The Nature of Technology

- Measuring instruments can be used to gather accurate information for making scientific comparisons of objects and events and for designing and constructing things that will work properly.
- There is no perfect design. Designs that are best in one respect (safety or ease of use, for example) may be inferior in other ways (cost or appearance). Usually some features must be sacrificed to get others. How such trade-offs are received depends upon which features are emphasized and which are down-played.
- Even a good design may fail. Sometimes steps can be taken ahead of time to reduce the likelihood of failure, but it cannot be entirely eliminated.
- Any invention is likely to lead to other inventions. Once an invention exists, people are likely to think up ways of using it that were never imagined at first.
- Technologies often have drawbacks as well as benefits. A technology that helps some people or organisms may hurt others—either deliberately (as weapons can) or inadvertently (as pesticides can). When harm occurs or seems likely, choices have to be made or new solutions found.
- People can use objects and ways of doing things to solve problems.

The Physical Setting

- Air is a substance that surrounds us, takes up space, and whose movement we feel as wind.
- Heating and cooling cause changes in the properties of materials. Many kinds of changes occur faster under hotter conditions.
- When warmer things are put with cooler ones, the warm ones lose heat and the cool ones gain it until they are all at the same temperature. A warmer object can warm a cooler one by contact or at a distance.
- Some materials conduct heat much better than others. Poor conductors can reduce heat loss.
- "Students should have lots of experiences to shape their intuition about motion and forces long before encountering laws. Especially helpful are experimentation and discussion of what happens as surfaces become more elastic or more free of friction." (pg. 88)
- Something that is moving may move steadily or change its direction. The greater the force is, the greater the change in motion will be. The more massive an object is, the less effect a given force will have.
- The earth's gravity pulls any object toward it without touching it.

v

- Without touching them, a magnet pulls on all things made of iron and either pushes or pulls on other magnets.
- Without touching them, material that has been electrically charged pulls on all other materials and may either push or pull other charged materials.

The Designed World
- Moving air and water can be used to run machines.
- Some energy sources cost less than others and some cause less pollution than others.
- People try to conserve energy in order to slow down the depletion of energy resources and/or to save money.

The Mathematical World
- Measurements are always likely to give slightly different numbers, even if what is being measured stays the same.
- Tables and graphs can show how values of one quantity are related to values of another.
- Graphical display of numbers may make it possible to spot patterns that are not otherwise obvious, such as comparative size and trends.
- Scale drawings show shapes and compare locations of things very different in size.

Common Themes
- Even in some very simple systems, it may not always be possible to predict accurately the result of changing some part or connection.
- Seeing how a model works after changes are made to it may suggest how the real thing would work if the same were done to it.
- Geometric figures, number sequences, graphs, diagrams, sketches, number lines, maps, and stories can be used to represent objects, events, and processes in the real world, although such representations can never be exact in every detail.

Habits of Mind
- Raise questions about the world around them and be willing to seek answers to some of them by making careful observations and trying things out.
- Offer reasons for their findings and consider reasons suggested by others.
- Make something out of paper, cardboard, wood, plastic, metal, or existing objects that can actually be used to perform a task.
- Make sketches to aid in explaining procedures or ideas.
- Buttress their statements with facts found in books, articles, and databases, and identify the sources used and expect others to do the same.
- Recognize when comparisons might not be fair because some conditions are not kept the same.

American Association for the Advancement of Science. *Benchmarks for Science Literacy.* Oxford University Press. New York. 1993.

Science as Inquiry
- Ask a question about objects, organisms, and events in the environment.
- Employ simple equipment and tools to gather data and extend the senses.
- Communicate investigations and explanations.
- Scientists use different kinds of investigations depending on the questions they are trying to answer. Types of investigations include describing objects, events, and organisms; classifying them; and doing a fair test (experimenting).

Physical Science
- Objects have many observable properties, including, size, weight, shape, color, temperature, and the ability to react with other substances. Those properties can be measured using tools, such as rulers, balances, and thermometers.
- Objects are made of one or more materials, such as paper, wood, and metal. Objects can be described by the properties of the materials from which they are made, and those properties can be used to separate or sort a group of objects or materials.
- Materials can exist in different states—solid, liquid, and gas. Some common materials, such as water, can be changed from one state to another by heating or cooling.
- The position of an object can be described by locating it relative to another object or the background.
- An object's motion can be described by tracing and measuring its position over time.
- The position and motion of objects can be changed by pushing or pulling. The size of the change is related to the strength of the push or pull.
- The motion of an object can be described by its position, direction of motion, and speed. That motion can be measured and represented on a graph.
- Heat can be produced in many ways, such as burning, rubbing, or mixing one substance with another. Heat can move from one object to another by conduction.
- Heat moves in predictable ways, flowing from warmer objects to cooler ones, until both reach the same temperature.
- Magnets attract and repel each other and certain kinds of other materials.

Life Science
- The behavior of individual organisms is influenced by internal cues (such as hunger) and by external cues (such as a change in the environment). Humans and other organisms have senses that help them detect internal and external cues.

Science and Technology
- Design a solution or product.
- Evaluate a product or design.
- People have always had problems and invented tools and techniques (way of doing something) to solve problems. Trying to determine the effects of solutions helps people avoid some new problems.
- Some objects occur in nature; others have been designed and made by people to solve human problems and enhance the quality of life.
- Technological solutions have intended benefits and unintended consequences. Some consequences can be predicted, others cannot.

Science in Personal and Social Perspectives
- Resources are things that we get from the living and nonliving environment to meet the needs and wants of a population.
- The supply of many resources is limited. If used, resources can be extended through recycling and decreased use.
- People continue inventing new ways of doing things, solving problems, and getting work done. New ideas and inventions often affect other people; sometimes the effects are good and sometimes they are bad. It is helpful to try to determine in advance how ideas and inventions will affect other people.
- Science and technology have advanced through contributions of many different people, in different cultures, at different times in history. Science and technology have contributed enormously to economic growth and productivity among societies and groups within societies.

History and Nature of Science
- Science and technology have been practiced by people for a long time.

National Research Council. *National Science Education Standards*. National Academy Press. Washington D.C. 1996.

NCTM Standards 2000

Number and Operations
• Develop fluency in adding, subtracting, multiplying, and dividing whole numbers

Algebra
• Describe, extend, and make generalizations about geometric and numeric patterns
• Model problem situations with objects and use representations such as graphs, tables, and equations to draw conclusions

Geometry
• Describe, name, and interpret direction and distance in navigating space and apply ideas about direction and distance
• Describe location and movement using common language and geometric vocabulary

Measurement
• Understand how to measure using nonstandard and standard units
• Select and apply appropriate standard units and tools to measure length, area, volume, weight, time, temperature, and the size of angles
• Select and use benchmarks to estimate measurements

Data Analysis and Probability
• Collect data using observations, surveys, and experiments
• Represent data using tables and graphs such as line plots, bar graphs, and line graphs
• Use measures of center, focusing on the median, and understand what each does and does not indicate about the data set
• Propose and justify conclusions and predictions that are based on data and design studies to further investigate the conclusions or predictions

Problem Solving
• Solve problems that arise in mathematics and in other contexts

Connections
• Recognize and apply mathematics in contexts outside of mathematics

Representation
• Use representations to model and interpret physical, social, and mathematical phenomena

National Geography Standards

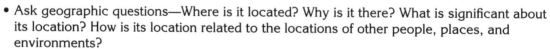
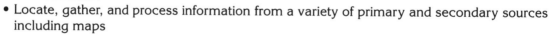

• Ask geographic questions—Where is it located? Why is it there? What is significant about its location? How is its location related to the locations of other people, places, and environments?
• Locate, gather, and process information from a variety of primary and secondary sources including maps

Scientific Inquiry

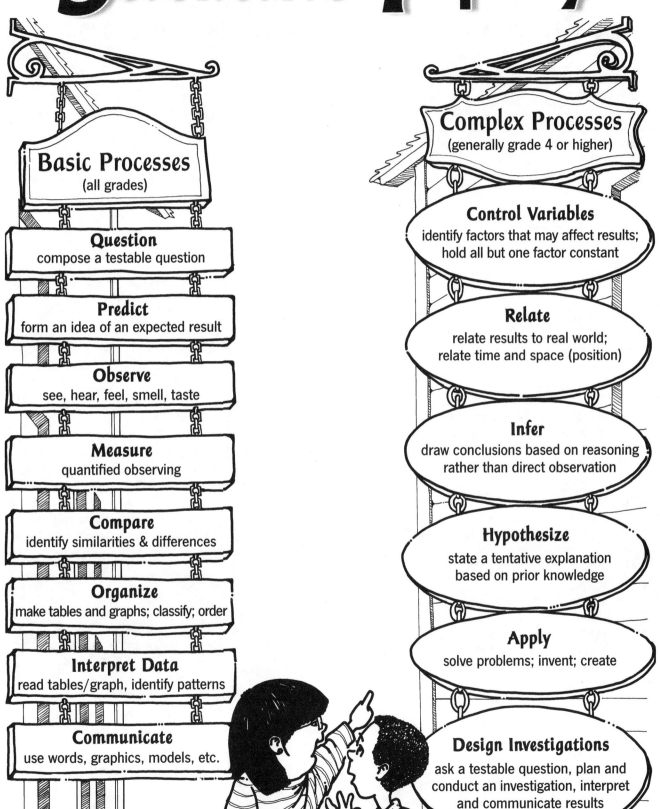

Basic Processes
(all grades)

Question
compose a testable question

Predict
form an idea of an expected result

Observe
see, hear, feel, smell, taste

Measure
quantified observing

Compare
identify similarities & differences

Organize
make tables and graphs; classify; order

Interpret Data
read tables/graph, identify patterns

Communicate
use words, graphics, models, etc.

Complex Processes
(generally grade 4 or higher)

Control Variables
identify factors that may affect results;
hold all but one factor constant

Relate
relate results to real world;
relate time and space (position)

Infer
draw conclusions based on reasoning
rather than direct observation

Hypothesize
state a tentative explanation
based on prior knowledge

Apply
solve problems; invent; create

Design Investigations
ask a testable question, plan and
conduct an investigation, interpret
and communicate results

Scientific Inquiry

Basic Processes

Question
Ask a question that can be tested. First-hand experiences are the catalyst for generating interesting questions. Investigations providing answers to these questions lead to new questions. Knowledge is continually constructed and refined.

Predict
Form an idea of an expected result, usually an action or behavior. A prediction is more than a guess; current knowledge is used to project whether a future event will occur. It does not require the reasoning and prior data needed to hypothesize.

Observe
Examine the properties or attributes of objects and their interactions using the five senses.

Measure
Make quantitative observations of objects by comparing to standard or non-standard units. Skills include knowing how to use various measuring tools, recognizing scale increments, determining the degree of preciseness required, and reading quantities carefully.

Compare
Identify qualitative and quantitative similarities and differences among objects or events. Measurement is a form of comparison.

Organize
Compile, classify, and order observed data, i.e., make tables, systematically group objects/data according to shared characteristics, arrange objects/data in order, and /or illustrate data with the appropriate graph.

Interpret Data
Analyze data by reading tables and graphs. Identify patterns or relationships in the data.

Communicate
Convey information and insights orally, in writing, pictorially, graphically, symbolically, or with models. Communication is an essential part of all the processes.

Complex Processes

Control Variables
Become aware of all of the possibilities that can affect the results. Hold all but one of these factors or characteristics constant.

Relate
Connect results to experiences in the real world. At a more advanced level, understand events in which time is linked to space (position/motion). The latter is exemplified by pendulums, Earth's revolution around the sun, acceleration studies, etc.

Infer
Draw conclusions or generalize based on reasoning rather than direct observation.

Hypothesize
Construct a tentative explanation using reasoning or logic, based on data gathered from prior experiences.

Apply
Solve problems. Invent. Create.

Design an Investigation
Ask a testable *question,* plan the investigation, conduct the investigation (*predict, observe, measure, compare, organize),* and *interpret* and *communicate* the results. Incorporates all of the basic processes and will likely include complex processes such as *controlling variables.*

Scientific Inquiry

Guided Scientific Inquiry

Scientific inquiry is questioning which leads to active investigation, via a series of processes, in search of answers. Most AIMS activities are supported by student pages with questions, tables, graphs, and procedural information, simplifying implementation. These provide a wealth of practice with guided inquiry.

Steps Toward Self-Directed Scientific Inquiry

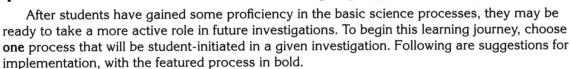
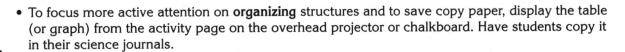

After students have gained some proficiency in the basic science processes, they may be ready to take a more active role in future investigations. To begin this learning journey, choose **one** process that will be student-initiated in a given investigation. Following are suggestions for implementation, with the featured process in bold.

- To focus more active attention on **organizing** structures and to save copy paper, display the table (or graph) from the activity page on the overhead projector or chalkboard. Have students copy it in their science journals.

- To further develop **organizing** skills, block out the table on the activity page before making copies. Have students construct their own tables in the open space. Guide discussion about what and how much data needs to be gathered, what table headings best describe the data, and how the headings should be positioned.

- Another option for working on **organizing** skills deals with graphing. If students are acquainted with a variety of graphs (bar graphs for discrete data, line graphs for change over time, circle graphs for part/whole relationships, etc.), block out the graph on the activity page before making copies. Ask students to choose the appropriate graph for the data and guide them in constructing it, complete with graph title and labels.

- To become more aware of **measuring** issues, first have students experience the action to be studied, such as a ball bounce. Then ask students questions such as: "What kind of measurement do we need to take? What could affect our measurement? What do we need to know to properly use the measuring tool? [where to place the tool, identify the scale increments, read at eye level, read carefully, etc.] To what unit will we round our measurement reading?"

- To work on **controlling variables,** have students perform the action to be examined in the activity, for example, using a catapult. Ask the class what kinds of things could affect the results and encourage them to brainstorm the possibilities. Explain that only one variable is tested at a time. "How can we make sure our test is fair?" [Keep all the other variables the same.] Guide students in identifying how they will control all but one variable.

- To set the stage for **questioning,** give students time to explore the action to be investigated, such as a pendulum swing. From this exploration, have students brainstorm questions that can be tested.

Self-Directed Scientific Inquiry

After sufficient experience with guided inquiry, followed by semi-guided inquiry as suggested above, students may be ready to **design** their own **investigations.** Students can use the questions on the next page as a guide in their planning.

Some AIMS activities are purposely written in a less guided or more open-ended manner and challenge students to develop their own plan of action.

Scientific Inquiry

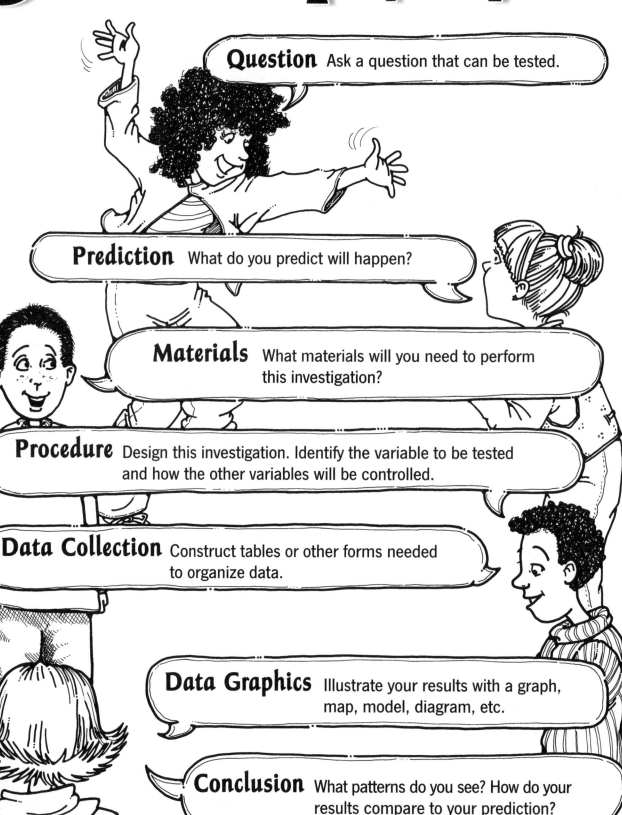

Question Ask a question that can be tested.

Prediction What do you predict will happen?

Materials What materials will you need to perform this investigation?

Procedure Design this investigation. Identify the variable to be tested and how the other variables will be controlled.

Data Collection Construct tables or other forms needed to organize data.

Data Graphics Illustrate your results with a graph, map, model, diagram, etc.

Conclusion What patterns do you see? How do your results compare to your prediction?

4

Have a Ball

Have a Ball (ball type) is the first of three activities isolating different variables that affect the bounce of a ball. It is followed by *On the Rebound* (drop height) and *From the Ground Up* (surface).

Topics
Scientific inquiry
Mechanical energy

Key Question
How does the bounce of different balls compare?

Learning Goals
Students will:
• compare the bounce height of various balls, and
• evaluate the ball variables that may affect the bounce.

Guiding Documents
Project 2061 Benchmarks
• *Scientists' explanations about what happens in the world come partly from what they observe, partly from what they think. Sometimes scientists have different explanations for the same set of observations. That usually leads to their making more observations to resolve the differences.*
• *Results of scientific investigations are seldom exactly the same, but if the differences are large, it is important to try to figure out why. One reason for following directions carefully and for keeping records of one's work is to provide information on what might have caused the differences.*
• *Measurements are always likely to give slightly different numbers, even if what is being measured stays the same.*

NRC Standards
• *Employ simple equipment and tools to gather data and extend the senses.*
• *Communicate investigations and explanations.*
• *An object's motion can be described by tracing and measuring its position over time.*

NCTM Standards 2000*
• *Select and apply appropriate standard units and tools to measure length, area, volume, weight, time, temperature, and the size of angles*
• *Use measures of center, focusing on the median, and understand what each does and does not indicate about the data set*
• *Propose and justify conclusions and predictions that are based on data and design studies to further investigate the conclusions or predictions.*

Math
Measurement
 length
 mass
Ordering
Median average
Graph
 bar

Science
Scientific inquiry
Physical science
 force and motion
 mechanical energy

Integrated Processes
Predicting
Observing
Controlling variables
Collecting and recording data
Comparing and contrasting
Interpreting data

Materials
For each group:
 5 sports balls (see *Management 1*)
 meter stick
 balance
 metric masses
 tape measure or string
 crayons or colored pencils

Background Information
Scientific inquiry
 The focus in this activity is not so much on the content of science as on the processes of science. A question is posed and students observe, measure, organize, and interpret data to answer the question. The results should then raise further questions: What variables might have affected the results?
 The variables of surface and height are controlled; the same surface and the same height are used for all of the ball drops. So attention turns to differences between the balls (manipulated or independent variable), attributes such as mass, circumference, and composition. Is there a relationship between bounce height (responding or dependent variable) and one or more of these attributes?

5

While circumference and mass can play a role, the composition of the ball most influences the height of the bounce. Watching a stop-action replay in tennis, you can see how a tennis ball is deformed on impact. The materials with which the ball is composed allow it to be flattened to some degree. The ball's spring as it returns back to its normal shape propels the bounce upward.

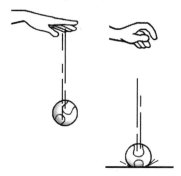

Mechanical energy

In terms of science content, the bounce of various balls is in the realm of physical science. It is about force and motion, with gravity being the force behind the motion of the ball. It is about mechanical energy, both potential and kinetic.

The following brief discussion of mechanical energy is offered for teacher background and may not be developmentally appropriate to share with students. An elevated ball has *gravitational potential energy*, energy stored and ready to do work. When it is released, gravity causes the ball to fall. The gravitational potential energy changes into *kinetic energy*, the energy of motion. As the ball hits the surface, kinetic energy deforms it, similar to the way a spring is compressed. Some of the energy changes to sound energy (the sound of the ball hitting the surface), some is converted to heat energy (heat generated by friction between the ball and surface), and some is absorbed by the surface itself. As the ball springs back to its normal shape, it is propelled upward (kinetic energy). Because some energy is lost at impact, the ball does not bounce back up to its drop height.

Management

1. Collect at least two duplicate sets of five balls. Choose from small rubber balls, superballs, basketballs, soccer balls, volleyballs, softballs, tennis balls, golf balls, table tennis balls, etc. The balls can be passed from group to group or, if there are enough sets, each group can have its own.
2. Have the other materials available for groups to gather.
3. Locate a hard surface, such as concrete, that can be used by all of the groups.
4. Jobs should be rotated so each group member has a chance to be the ball dropper, the measurer, and the recorder.

5. Since it is difficult to take measurements of objects in motion, an average taken of multiple trials is likely to yield more reliable results. Younger children should order the three trial measurements on scratch paper and circle the middle one (median average). Older children may add the three measurements and divide by three to find the mean.
6. Suggestions for moving toward self-directed inquiry can be found on the page, *Scientific Inquiry: Guided to Self-Directed*.
7. To have students practice **questioning**, block out the *More Data* table before making copies of the second page. Suggest they think of ball variables and compose a testable question such as "Does the mass of a ball affect how high it will bounce?" Then have them proceed with collecting data.

Procedure

1. Hold up two balls and ask "How are these balls different?" Have students make observations. Ask them to predict which ball will bounce highest and explain why they made that prediction.
2. Distribute the first activity page to each student or group. Instruct them to record their predictions and reasons.
3. Discuss how two variables will be kept the same, surface and drop height, and have students record these. Choose a drop height between 100 to 150 centimeters.
4. To help ensure fair testing, review measurement procedures. Drop height and bounce height are measured from the surface to the bottom of the ball. Hold the bottom of the ball even with the designated height and let it drop; do not throw or push. Temporarily mark the bounce height on the meter stick with a finger or pencil. Record to the nearest centimeter.

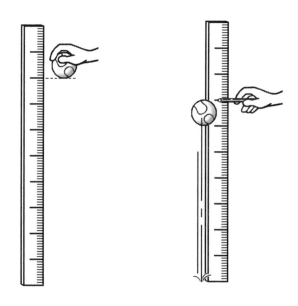

5. Have groups gather materials, collect data, and complete the table.

6. Give students the second activity page. Guide them in labeling and numbering the bar graph, then completing the graph and ordering the results. If a 100-cm drop height and increments of five are used, the bounces can be compared to the drop height (top graph line).

7. Ask one group to order a set of balls from highest to lowest bounce. Encourage groups to compare their results with this display and with their original predictions. Discrepancies point to the need for further testing.

8. Field new questions based on the results such as, "Are any of the balls' attributes related to bounce height?" Have students measure and record observations in the *More Data* table, describing composition as best they can.

9. After studying this table, have groups discuss and then write their conclusions.

Connecting Learning

1. How are these balls alike? [spheres] How are they different? [circumference, mass, composition, color, markings, texture, air-filled or not, etc.]

2. We measured circumference, mass, and bounce height. Which was easiest to measure? Which was most difficult? Explain.

3. How do you know this was a fair test? [The way the ball was released, the kind of surface, and the drop height were kept the same. Only the type of ball was different.]

4. How did bounce height compare to drop height?

5. What attribute most affected the height of the bounce? Why is further testing a good idea? [The larger the sample, the more reliable the results.]

6. Which part of this activity did you enjoy most? What surprised you?

7. In what other ways could the bounce be tested? [try different surfaces or different drop heights] Make a plan to test one of these.

* Reprinted with permission from *Principles and Standards for School Mathematics,* 2000 by the National Council of Teachers of Mathematics. All rights reserved.

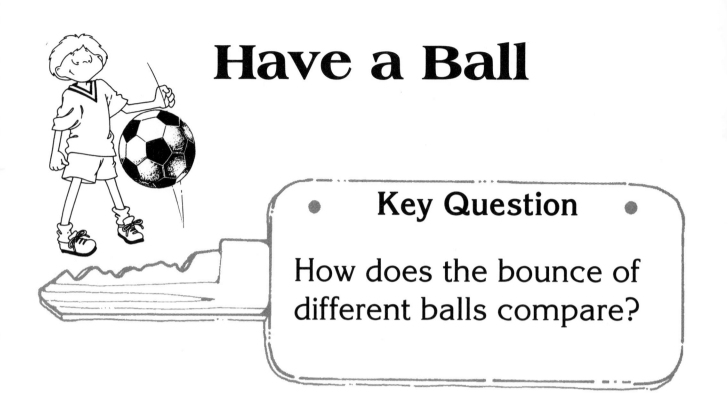

Have a Ball

Key Question

How does the bounce of different balls compare?

Learning Goals

Students will:

- compare the bounce height of various sports balls, and
- evaluate the ball variables that may affect the bounce.

Have a Ball

**How does the bounce of
different balls compare?**

Prediction

What is your prediction?

Why did you make this prediction?

Variables Controlled

Surface:
Drop Height:

Data Collection

Ball	Height of Bounce			Average

(median or mean)

Have a Ball

Graph

Results

highest bounce

lowest bounce

More Data

Mass	Circumference	Composition

Conclusions

Have a Ball

1. How are these balls alike? How are they different?

2. We measured circumference, mass, and bounce height. Which was easiest to measure? Which was most difficult? Explain.

3. How do you know this was a fair test?

4. How did bounce height compare to drop height?

5. What attribute most affected the height of the bounce? Why is further testing a good idea?

6. Which part of this activity did you enjoy most? What surprised you?

7. In what other ways could the bounce be tested? Make a plan to test one of these.

On the Rebound

Topics
Algebraic thinking: patterns
Force and motion

Key Question
How does the ball's bounce compare with drop height?

Learning Goal
Students will discover a pattern relating the height from which a ball is dropped to the height of its bounce.

Guiding Documents
Project 2061 Benchmarks
• *Mathematics is the study of many kinds of patterns, including numbers and shapes and operations on them. Sometimes patterns are studied because they help to explain how the world works or how to solve practical problems, sometimes because they are interesting in themselves.*
• *Graphical display of numbers may make it possible to spot patterns that are not otherwise obvious, such as comparative size and trends.*
• *The earth's gravity pulls any object toward it without touching it.*

NRC Standards
• *Employ simple equipment and tools to gather data and extend the senses.*
• *An object's motion can be described by tracing and measuring its position over time.*

NCTM Standards 2000*
• *Select and apply appropriate standard units and tools to measure length, area, volume, weight, time, temperature, and the size of angles*
• *Use measures of center, focusing on the median, and understand what each does and does not indicate about the data set*
• *Describe, extend, and make generalizations about geometric and numeric patterns*

Math
Estimation
Measurement
    length
Median average
Graph
    bar to line
Algebraic thinking

Science
Physical science
    force and motion

Integrated Processes
Observing
Collecting and recording data
Comparing and contrasting
Interpreting data

Materials
For each group:
    golf ball
    meter stick
    small pieces of paper

Background Information
Algebraic Thinking
    Children can engage in algebraic thinking at a very young age. Whenever pre-kindergarteners sort, they are applying a rule they or someone else has made; that is algebraic thinking. Whenever a red-blue-red-blue bead pattern is discovered and extended, algebraic thinking is being exercised. As children develop, it is hoped they will be challenged by more advanced sorting and patterning activities such as this one. All of these experiences with patterns form a foundation for the more formal generalization of patterns studied in algebra.
    Algebraic thinking is about detecting patterns, extending patterns, and—at its highest level—generalizing patterns. Many patterning experiences are done with stationary objects. Here students look for a pattern of motion determined from a series of measurements. Then they are asked to extend the pattern.
    Motion increases the difficulty of measuring precisely. The ball does not freeze at the highest point of its bounce. The observer has to quickly determine when the highest point is reached and also try to read the measuring scale as carefully as possible. There is certainly room for error. Measurement is approximate, since it can be taken to another, more precise decimal place.
    We want students to get excited about finding patterns. There *is* a relationship between drop height and bounce height for a given ball striking a given surface, at least within the drop heights explored in this activity. A line graph is appropriate for this kind of data. To aid understanding, students first construct the more familiar bar graph and then convert it into a line graph. The line is useful for estimating the bounces from drop heights between and beyond—if the line is extended—those shown on the graph. A straight line indicates a generalized pattern.

Force and Motion

A force is a push or a pull. Students intuitively know that the ball will drop to the ground. The force of gravity is pulling the ball toward the Earth. Students may also intuitively know that the higher the drop, the higher the bounce. The farther the ball falls, the greater the speed at which it strikes the surface. The greater the speed, the higher the rebound. For the drop heights explored in this activity, this holds true.

Management

1. Organize the class into groups of three. Jobs might include measurer, ball dropper, and recorder.
2. Height is defined as the distance from the surface to the bottom of the ball.
3. To gather data, hold the meter stick vertically or tape it to a wall or pole. Hold the bottom of the ball even with the designated height and let it drop.
4. Use a concrete surface if possible.
5. Since higher bounces are easier to measure, the table starts with the 100-cm drop. The experience gained will be useful as the drop height is lowered.
6. After students have measured several bounce heights, you may want to challenge them to estimate the next bounces. They also practice estimation when deciding where 63, for example, should be on the graph marked in increments of five.
7. For suggestions leading toward self-directed inquiry, see *Scientific Inquiry: Guided to Self-Directed.*

Procedure

1. Give each group a golf ball and ask students to drop it different distances from the floor. Ask, "What did you observe?" [The balls fall to the ground (gravity). They bounce back up, but not as high.] "How does the ball's bounce compare with drop height?"
2. Distribute the activity page and instruct students to record the type of ball and surface (controlled variables).
3. Give each group a meter stick and direct students to the locations where they will perform the investigation.
4. To increase the chance of reliable results, have students record three trials at each drop height on the back of the page, order the three measurements, and record the middle number (median average) in the table.
5. Instruct students to fill in the solid-line portion of the bar graph.
6. To convert the bar graph into a line graph, have students make a dot at the top center of each colored bar and connect the dots.

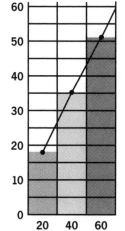

7. After students have studied the graph, ask questions such as:
   • How would you describe the shape of the line on the graph? [fairly straight (depending on the preciseness of measurements)] Explain that a straight line means there is a pattern. A pattern is useful for making estimates.
   • If a ball is dropped from 70 cm, what do you estimate its bounce height would be? (Students should locate the line's position halfway between 60 and 80 cm.)
   • If a ball is dropped from 120 cm, how could you estimate its bounce height? [Extend the line.]
8. Have students write their estimates at the bottom of the page, then test and record the actual bounce based, once again, on the median average of three measurements.

Connecting Learning

1. Why is measuring the bounce a challenge? [The ball is in motion when you are trying to measure it so there is more chance of error. It requires the observer to make a split-second judgment about the highest point of the bounce and to know how to read the meter stick's scale.]
2. Why is a median average better than taking one bounce measurement? [The chance for reliable results increases by averaging several trials. A single measurement may be quite off the mark. Several measurements allow you to judge whether the results are consistent. With averaging, less precise measurements are tempered by more precise measurements.]
3. How do your group's results compare with others? (Variations in the accuracy of measurements and how well variables are controlled can cause differences.)
4. How is force involved when a ball is dropped? [The force of gravity causes the ball to fall.]
5. As the drop height is raised, what happens to the bounce? [The higher the drop height, the higher the bounce.]
6. What other things does the graph tell you? [A straight line means there is a pattern; the bounce height increases by about the same amount every time the drop height is raised. You can use the line to estimate bounces from other drop heights.]
7. What new questions do you have?

Extensions

1. Substitute another kind of ball and repeat the activity.
2. See the related activities, *Have a Ball* and *From the Ground Up.*

* Reprinted with permission from *Principles and Standards for School Mathematics,* 2000 by the National Council of Teachers of Mathematics. All rights reserved.

On the Rebound

Key Question

How does the ball's bounce compare with drop height?

Learning Goal

Students will:

- discover a pattern relating the height from which a ball is dropped to the height of its bounce.

On the Rebound

How does the ball's bounce compare with drop height?

Type of ball:

Type of surface:

Drop height	Bounce height*
100 cm	
80 cm	
60 cm	
40 cm	
20 cm	

*median average of three trials

The Unknown Bounce

Use the graph to estimate the bounce height of a ball dropped from 120 cm.

Estimate:

Actual:

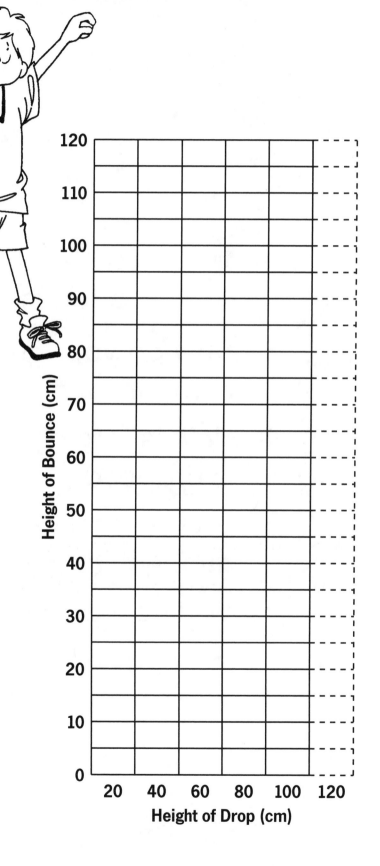

On the Rebound

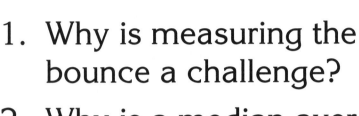

1. Why is measuring the bounce a challenge?

2. Why is a median average better than taking one bounce measurement?

3. How do your group's results compare with others?

4. How is force involved when a ball is dropped?

5. As the drop height is raised, what happens to the bounce?

6. What other things does the graph tell you?

7. What new questions do you have?

From the Gr⊙und Up

Topics
Scientific inquiry
Mechanical energy

Key Question
What effect does surface have on bounce height?

Learning Goal
Students will discover how the kind of surfaces on which a ball is dropped affects how high it will bounce.

Guiding Documents
Project 2061 Benchmarks
- *Scientists' explanations about what happens in the world come partly from what they observe, partly from what they think. Sometimes scientists have different explanations for the same set of observations. That usually leads to their making more observations to resolve the differences.*
- *Offer reasons for their findings and consider reasons suggested by others.*

NRC Standards
- *Employ simple equipment and tools to gather data and extend the senses.*
- *An object's motion can be described by tracing and measuring its position over time.*

NCTM Standards 2000*
- *Select and apply appropriate standard units and tools to measure length, area, volume, weight, time, temperature, and the size of angles*
- *Use measures of center, focusing on the median, and understand what each does and does not indicate about the data set*

Math
Measurement
    length
Ordering
Median average

Science
Physical science
    mechanical energy

Integrated Processes
Observing
Predicting
Collecting and recording data
Comparing and contrasting
Controlling variables
Interpreting data

Materials
For each group:
    golf ball
    meter stick

Background Information
Think of the ball as having an energy bank account. As the ball is being held above the ground, it has a given amount of energy. If no energy is "spent" when the dropped ball hits the surface, it would bounce back up to its starting height. At impact, however, some of the ball's energy *is* spent. Some changes to sound energy, the sound of the ball hitting the surface. Some is converted to heat generated by friction between the ball and the surface. Some is absorbed by the surface itself. The more energy that is spent, the lower the bounce. Surfaces that absorb the least energy allow the ball to bounce highest.

Management
1. Make sure students use only one type of ball. A golf ball is recommended.
2. Divide the class into groups of three. They can rotate through the locations with different surfaces.
3. Height is defined as the distance from the surface to the bottom of the ball.
4. To gather data, hold the meter stick vertically or tape it to a wall or pole. Hold the bottom of the ball even with the designated height and let it drop.
5. Since it is difficult to take measurements of objects in motion, an average taken of multiple trials is likely to yield more reliable results. Have students order the three trial measurements on scratch paper and circle the middle one (median average).
6. Choose surfaces such as concrete, carpet, dirt, blacktop, wood, floor tiles, foam pad, grass, metal plate, cardboard, etc.
7. To take a step toward self-directed inquiry, try one of the suggestions on the page, *Scientific Inquiry: Guided to Self-Directed.*

Procedure

1. Have students brainstorm kinds of surfaces found around school. Pick five to use in the investigation.
2. Distribute the activity page and instruct students to record the type of ball and drop height to be used. Have them order their predictions of surfaces from highest bounce to lowest bounce.
3. Direct groups to conduct the tests and record their data in the table.
4. Ask students to order the results in the *Actual* column.
5. Discuss the results and introduce the idea of an energy bank account.

Connecting Learning

1. How do you know this was a fair test? [The way the ball was released, the type of ball, and the height of the drop were kept the same. Only one variable, the kind of surface, was examined. A well-designed and fair scientific study tests only one variable at a time.]
2. How does the bounce compare to the starting height? [The bounce is lower than the starting height.] Why does this happen? [Some of the ball's energy is spent when it hits the surface, so there is less energy for the ball to bounce back to its original height.]
3. Does the kind of surface on which a ball bounces matter? Explain. [Yes. Different surfaces absorb different amounts of energy. The more energy they absorb, the lower the bounce.]
4. Do you think you could find a surface that would allow a ball to bounce as high as its starting height? Explain. [No. The ball would have to keep all the energy it started with and some energy is always changed or transferred when it strikes a surface.]
5. Would a ball ever bounce higher than its drop? Explain. [No, it would have to gain energy as it moved and this cannot happen.] What would happen if it could? [It would keep bouncing higher and higher and eventually go into outer space.]
6. What are you wondering now?

Extensions

1. Try sand as a surface. What happens? [It hardly bounces at all.] Why? [The sand absorbs the ball's energy.]
2. Using the same surfaces, try a different ball (racquetball, a steel ball bearing, tennis ball, superball, etc.). A steel ball on a steel plate has a very high bounce.
3. Have students summarize the results of *Have a Ball, On the Rebound,* and *From the Ground Up* by choosing the combination of variables that will give the highest bounce (the best ball, the best surface, and the best height of those tried).

* Reprinted with permission from *Principles and Standards for School Mathematics,* 2000 by the National Council of Teachers of Mathematics. All rights reserved.

From the Ground Up

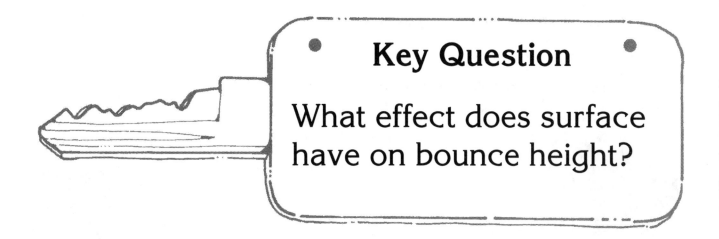

Key Question

What effect does surface have on bounce height?

Learning Goal

Students will:

- discover how the kind of surfaces on which a ball is dropped affects how high it will bounce.

From the Gr⬤und Up

What effect does surface have on bounce height?

Put the surfaces in order from highest bounce to lowest bounce.

Prediction	Actual

Type of ball:

Drop height:

Surface	Bounce Height*

*median average of three trials

What did you learn?

From the Gr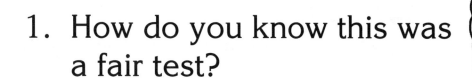und Up

CONNECTING LEARNING

1. How do you know this was a fair test?

2. How does the bounce compare to the starting height? Why does this happen?

3. Does the kind of surface on which a ball bounces matter? Explain.

4. Do you think you could find a surface that would allow a ball to bounce as high as its starting height? Explain.

5. Would a ball ever bounce higher than its drop? Explain. What would happen if it could?

6. What are you wondering now?

Swinging Bears

Part One

Topic
Pendulums

Key Question
How many cycles will your pendulum make in 30 seconds?

Learning Goal
Students will draw conclusions about the variable that affects the number of pendulum cycles.

Guiding Documents
Project 2061 Benchmarks
- *The earth's gravity pulls any object toward it without touching it.*
- *Mathematics is the study of many kinds of patterns, including numbers and shapes and operations on them. Sometimes patterns are studied because they help to explain how the world works or how to solve practical problems, sometimes because they are interesting in themselves.*

NRC Standard
- *An object's motion can be described by tracing and measuring its position over time.*

NCTM Standard 2000*
- *Collect data using observations, surveys, and experiments*

Math
Measurement
   length
Graph

Science
Physical science
   pendulums
   gravity

Integrated Processes
Observing
Collecting and recording data
Comparing and contrasting
Predicting
Interpreting data
Relating

Materials
For the class:
   number line from 1-50
   clock with second hand
   pushpins

For each group:
   2 Friendly Bears or Teddy Bear Counters
   2 pieces of string (see *Management 2*)
   masking tape

Background Information
Pendulums were first studied in depth by Galileo in the sixteenth century. He discovered the regular motion of pendulums while watching a lamp swaying in a cathedral in Pisa. Using his pulse to time the swing of the lamp, he found that although the arc through which the lamp swung steadily got smaller, its *period* (the time it took to make one complete out and back cycle) remained constant.

Fascinated by this experience, Galileo began to study pendulums. By careful observation and experimentation, he made several important discoveries. For one thing, he found that the length of the pendulum determined its *frequency* (cycles per minute): the longer the pendulum, the greater its period, and consequently, the lower its frequency. Secondly, he found that in order to predict the frequency of a pendulum, its length must be measured from its pivot point to its center of mass. Thirdly, he discovered that varying the mass of a pendulum while keeping its length the same did not change its frequency. These discoveries led to the first accurate clock (built shortly after his death) and helped Newton formulate his laws of motion.

Management

1. This activity does not require a student page. Instead, students help create a real graph using their pendulums.
2. Strings for the pendulums need to be prepared ahead of time. Cut strings to random lengths between 10 and 70 cm. Make sure there is a good distribution of short, medium, and long strings. Each group needs two strings.
3. If Friendly Bears or Teddy Bear Counters are not available, pennies, paper clips, or other small, uniform objects can be substituted as pendulum bobs.
4. Students should work in groups of three or four.
5. Ahead of time, construct the number line and pin it along the top of a bulletin board as shown in the illustration. If a bulletin board is not available, write the numbers 1 to 50 across the top of a chalkboard. In this case, the pendulums will need to be taped to the chalkboard instead of pinned to the bulletin board.

Procedure

1. Give each group two strings, two bears, and some tape.
2. Show students how to make a pendulum by taping the bear to one end of the string and tying a knot (not a loop) in the other end.
3. Once the pendulums are made, have each group pick one pendulum and tell them they will count how many cycles (one complete out and back swing is a cycle) it makes in 30 seconds. Explain that the pendulum bobs should be started from about a 45° angle and that it is important that the top of the pendulum (the knot) be held as steady as possible.
4. After students have finished counting the number of cycles, use pushpins (poked through the knot) to help them hang the pendulums under the appropriate numbers on the number line as shown below.
5. Tell students to look at the graph and use it to predict how many cycles their second pendulums will make in 30 seconds.
6. After groups have made their predictions, they should count the cycles to see how close their predictions were and then hang the second pendulums on the graph.
7. Discuss the pendulum activity.

Connecting Learning

1. What generalizations about pendulums can you make? [The shorter the pendulum, the greater the frequency—the longer the pendulum, the lower the frequency.]
2. What patterns do you see in the graph? [The pendulums form a curved line.]

3. How did the graph help you in making your prediction for the second pendulum? [The length of the second pendulum can be compared to the lengths of the pendulums already on the graph. This comparison will enable a fairly accurate prediction to be made.]
4. What length would you need to make a pendulum to give you ten cycles in 30 seconds? How could you find out? [The graph can be used to estimate the length of pendulum needed.]
5. Why do you think pendulums are used in grandfather clocks and cuckoo clocks? [Since pendulums of a given length have a predictable (and constant) frequency, they help these clocks keep accurate time.]
6. The weight at the bottom of a grandfather clock's pendulum can be moved up and down. If the clock is running slow, what way should the weight be moved? Why? [The weight should be moved up. This shortens the length of the pendulum and increases its frequency.]
7. What other pendulum questions would you like to explore?

Extensions

1. Show the relationship between the pendulum graph and the acceleration due to gravity by gently throwing a ball horizontally in front of the graph, starting at the level of the shortest pendulum. If the ball is tossed at the right speed, its downward curve will match the curve made by the pendulums.
2. Have students devise experiments to answer some of their pendulum questions.
3. Go outside and observe the pendulum motion of the playground swing.

* Reprinted with permission from *Principles and Standards for School Mathematics*, 2000 by the National Council of Teachers of Mathematics. All rights reserved.

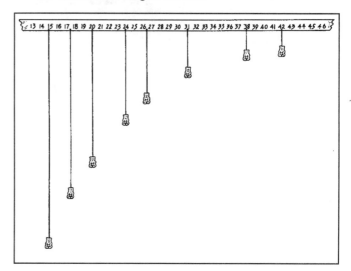

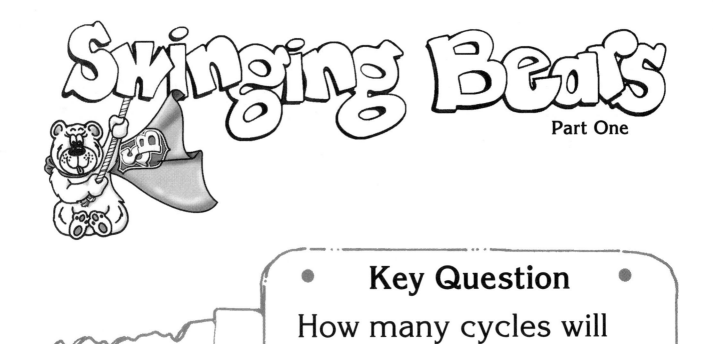

Swinging Bears

Part One

Learning Goal

Students will:

- draw conclusions about the variable that affects the number of pendulum cycles.

5 ⊕	10 ⊕	15 ⊕	20 ⊕	25 ⊕
4 ⊕	9 ⊕	14 ⊕	19 ⊕	24 ⊕
3 ⊕	8 ⊕	13 ⊕	18 ⊕	23 ⊕
2 ⊕	7 ⊕	12 ⊕	17 ⊕	22 ⊕
1 ⊕	6 ⊕	11 ⊕	16 ⊕	21 ⊕
	Tab	Tab	Tab	Tab

30 ⊕ 35 ⊕ 40 ⊕ 45 ⊕ 50 ⊕

29 ⊕ 34 ⊕ 39 ⊕ 44 ⊕ 49 ⊕

28 ⊕ 33 ⊕ 38 ⊕ 43 ⊕ 48 ⊕

27 ⊕ 32 ⊕ 37 ⊕ 42 ⊕ 47 ⊕

26 ⊕ 31 ⊕ 36 ⊕ 41 ⊕ 46 ⊕

Tab   Tab   Tab   Tab   Tab

Part One

On the chain tag: CONNECTING LEARNING

1. What generalizations about pendulums can you make?

2. What patterns do you see in the graph?

3. How did the graph help you in making your prediction for the second pendulum?

4. What length would you need to make a pendulum to give you ten cycles in 30 seconds? How could you find out?

5. Why do you think pendulums are used in grandfather clocks and cuckoo clocks?

6. The weight at the bottom of a grandfather clock's pendulum can be moved up and down. If the clock is running slow, what way should the weight be moved? Why?

7. What other pendulum questions would you like to explore?

Part Two

Topic
Pendulums

Key Question
How does changing the length of a pendulum affect its frequency?

Learning Goal
Students will explore the relationship between pendulum length and frequency.

Guiding Documents
Project 2061 Benchmarks
• *The earth's gravity pulls any object toward it without touching it.*
• *Mathematics is the study of many kinds of patterns, including numbers and shapes and operations on them. Sometimes patterns are studied because they help to explain how the world works or how to solve practical problems, sometimes because they are interesting in themselves.*

NRC Standard
• *An object's motion can be described by tracing and measuring its position over time.*

NCTM Standards 2000*
• *Select and apply appropriate standard units and tools to measure length, area, volume, weight, time, temperature, and the size of angles*
• *Represent data using tables and graphs such as line plots, bar graphs, and line graphs*

Math
Measurement
  length
Graph

Science
Physical science
  pendulums
  gravity

Integrated Processes
Observing
Collecting and recording data
Comparing and contrasting
Predicting
Drawing conclusions
Relating

Materials
For the class:
  clock or watch with second hand

For each group:
  1 Friendly Bear or Teddy Bear Counter
  65-100 cm piece of string
  masking tape
  meter stick or meter tape

Background Information
  The frequency of a pendulum is a function of its length: the shorter the length, the higher the frequency. See *Background Information* in *Swinging Bears, Part One.*

Management
1. *Swinging Bears, Part One* should be done before this activity.
2. Students need to know how to construct a line graph in order to do this activity.
3. Students should know the terms *cycle* (one complete out and back motion), *period* (the time for one cycle), and *frequency* (the number of cycles per minute).
4. Collaborative teams of three or four can collect data, but each student should have a copy of the activity page and graph page to record the team's results. Students can take turns with the various tasks: measuring the pendulum lengths, holding the pendulum, counting the cycles, and timing. If the string is held against the bottom edge of a table or desk, more accurate results are possible.

5. One string will be used for the various pendulum lengths. The length of each pendulum is measured from the pivot point to its center of mass (approximately the middle of the pendulum bobs). A meter stick should be used to carefully measure this distance for each different length. The loose end of the string should be placed on top of the table where it will be out of the way.

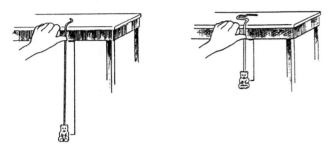

Changing Pendulum Lengths

6. The activity sheet and graph page are open-ended, allowing the teacher to choose the number and range of pendulum lengths to be tested.

7. Before doing the activity, decide on the pendulum lengths that will be used. A suggested range of lengths is 10 to 60 cm, with 10-cm increments. Longer pendulums can be used, but they will be too long to suspend from a table or desk. Pendulums shorter than 10 cm have high frequencies and are difficult to count.

8. Since the shorter pendulums have higher frequencies and are more difficult to count, it might be helpful to start the activity with the longer pendulums and finish with the shorter ones. This gives students practice in counting the cycles of the lower frequency pendulums first. Another way to make the counting easier is to time the pendulums for 30 seconds and double this number.

9. In making the graph, students should label the x-axis (horizontal) with the pendulum length (independent variable) and the y-axis (vertical) with the frequency (dependent variable). Scales for each axis should be chosen so that the maximum amount of graphing area is used.

Procedure
1. Ask the *Key Question* and state the *Learning Goal.*
2. Divide students into groups.
3. Give each group a string, tape, bear, and meter stick, as well as activity pages for each student.
4. Tell each group to tape their bear (or other small object) securely to one end of the string.
5. Have students record the pendulum lengths that will be tested in the appropriate boxes on the activity page.
6. Explain the process for measuring the various pendulum lengths and finding their frequencies.
7. Instruct students to do the activity and record their results on the page.
8. After discussing the results, have students write their observations and conclusions.
9. Direct students to use the collected data to construct a line graph, including numbers, labels, and a title.

Connecting Learning
1. What is the relationship between the length of a pendulum and its frequency? [They are inversely proportional; longer pendulums have lower frequencies.]
2. Which has a higher frequency, the pendulum on a grandfather clock or the one on a cuckoo clock? Why? [Cuckoo clocks have a higher frequency (one cycle per second) than grandfather clocks (one cycle every two seconds). This is because the pendulum on the cuckoo clock is shorter than the one on the grandfather clock.]
3. How would you use your graph to predict the frequencies of other pendulums? [The line graph allows you to see what frequencies in-between lengths (like 25 cm or 55 cm) would have.]
4. How does the line graph resemble the real graph made in *Swinging Bears, Part One?* [The line graph is like the real graph rotated 90 degrees to a vertical orientation.]
5. What other things have you learned from doing this activity?
6. What are you wondering now?

Extensions
1. Explore the history of clocks.
2. Read about Galileo and his study of pendulums.
3. Explore some other aspects of pendulums.

* Reprinted with permission from *Principles and Standards for School Mathematics,* 2000 by the National Council of Teachers of Mathematics. All rights reserved.

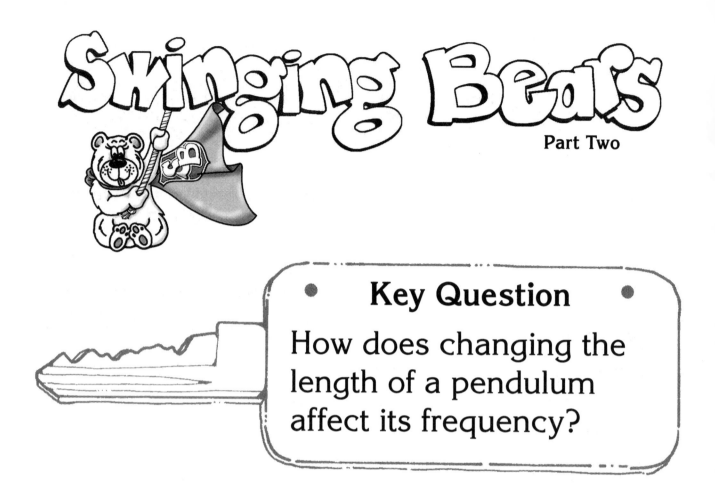

Swinging Bears

Part Two

Key Question

How does changing the length of a pendulum affect its frequency?

Learning Goal

Students will:

- explore the relationship between pendulum length and frequency.

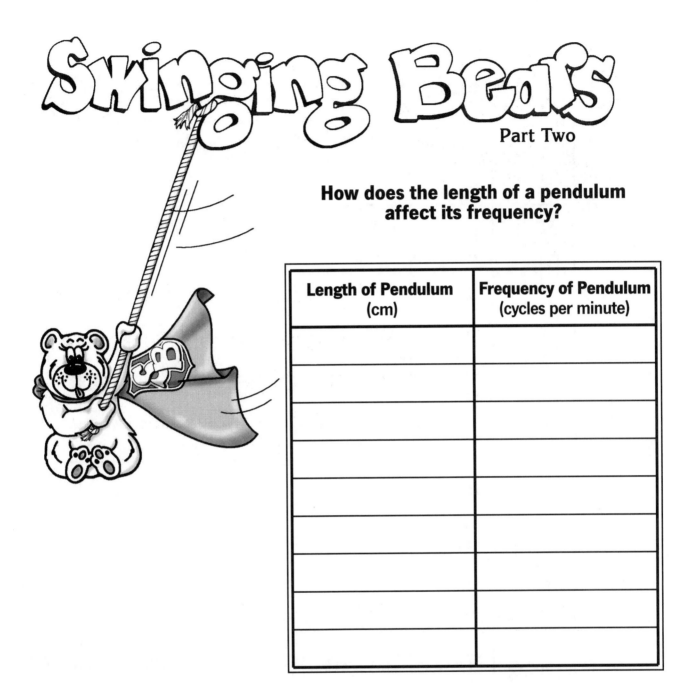

Swinging Bears

Part Two

How does the length of a pendulum affect its frequency?

Length of Pendulum (cm)	Frequency of Pendulum (cycles per minute)

What I learned:

My conclusions:

Swinging Bears

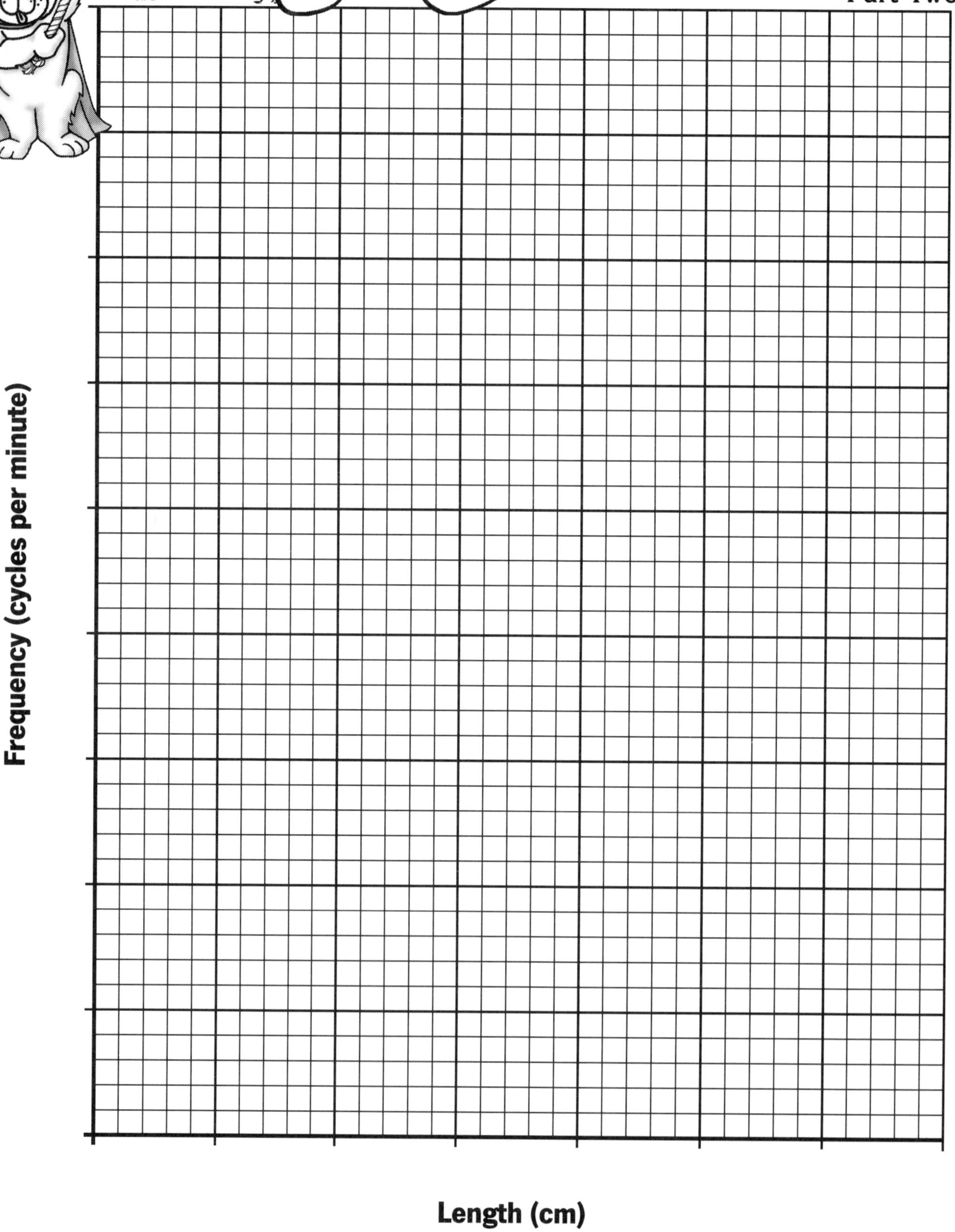

Frequency (cycles per minute)

Length (cm)

32

Swinging Bears

CONNECTING LEARNING

1. What is the relationship between the length of a pendulum and its frequency?

2. Which has a higher frequency, the pendulum on a grandfather clock or the one on a cuckoo clock? Why?

3. How would you use your graph to predict the frequencies of other pendulums?

4. How does the line graph resemble the real graph made in *Swinging Bears, Part One*?

5. What other things have you learned from doing this activity?

6. What are you wondering now?

33

Ball On a Roll

Topic
Mechanical energy

Key Question
How does the ball's height on the ramp affect the distance it rolls?

Learning Goals
Students will:
- explore how a ball's starting height on the ramp is related to the distance it rolls, and
- relate the downward movement of the ball to the force of gravity.

Guiding Documents
Project 2061 Benchmark
- *The earth's gravity pulls any object toward it without touching it.*

NRC Standards
- *An object's motion can be described by tracing and measuring its position over time.*
- *The position and motion of objects can be changed by pushing or pulling. The size of the change is related to the strength of the push or pull.*

NCTM Standards 2000*
- *Select and apply appropriate standard units and tools to measure length, area, volume, weight, time, temperature, and the size of angles*
- *Use measures of center, focusing on the median, and understand what each does and does not indicate about the data set*
- *Represent data using tables and graphs such as line plots, bar graphs, and line graphs*

Math
Estimation
Measurement
   length
Median average
Graph
   line

Science
Physical science
   mechanical energy
   gravity

Integrated Processes
Observing
Controlling variables
Collecting and recording data
Comparing and contrasting
Interpreting data

Materials
For each group:
   golf ball
   2 meter sticks (see *Management 1*)
   additional meter stick(s) or tape for measuring
   several books
   butcher paper
   masking tape
   cardboard, about 3" x 5"
   card stock, about 3" x 5"

Background Information
Dialoguing With Students: A Classroom Scenario

If I hold a pencil above me, what will happen when I let it go? [It will fall straight down.] Why? [Gravity will make it fall.] Gravity is a force that pulls the pencil downward. We live in a gravitational field. Just like a cornfield is where corn grows, a gravitational field is where there is gravity.

What does the word *potential* mean? [It means it could happen.] (Hold a ball on the ramp at 30 cm.) This ball has potential energy, energy ready to be used. It would move if I stopped holding it. The energy is not released until I let it go. This kind of potential energy is called *gravitational potential energy*, the energy an object has due to its position in a gravitational field. The higher the ball is from the floor, the more potential energy it has. A ball held at 70 cm on the ramp has more potential energy than a ball held at 30 cm.

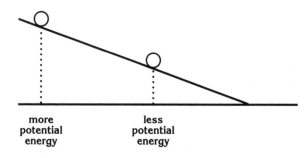

Height makes the difference.

How does the change from potential to kinetic energy happen? A ball held at a given position on the ramp has potential energy, but no kinetic energy.

As the ball rolls down the ramp, the potential energy changes into *kinetic energy,* the energy of motion. Halfway down the ramp, half of the potential energy has been changed into kinetic energy. By the time the ball reaches the bottom of the ramp, all of the available potential energy has been converted into kinetic energy. The higher the ball's starting position, the more potential energy it has to convert to kinetic energy and the farther the ball will travel once it leaves the ramp. It is the starting height that matters, not the length the ball will travel down the ramp.

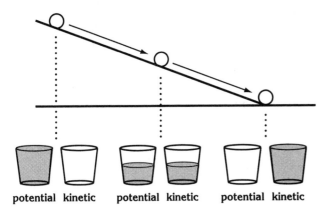

Change from potential to kinetic energy

Management

1. For the ramp, use meter sticks that do not flex or about 1-meter lengths of wood. Tape the sticks at three or four places along the length, leaving a gap of about 2 cm between the sticks. If not using meter sticks, mark 10-centimeter increments on the wood.

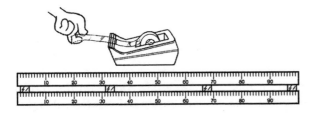

2. To set up the ramps, stack several books to a height of 10-12 centimeters. All ramps should be the same height. Place the 90-centimeter mark on the edge of the book stack, taped side at the bottom.

3. To minimize the drop-off bounce at the end of the ramp, tape thick cardstock strips flush with the surface of the sticks.

4. Roll out the butcher paper to at least 6 meters, more if testing positions above 60 centimeters. To keep the ball from straying, fold the edges of the paper up about 2 centimeters.

5. To ensure a standard release of the ball, use a small piece of cardboard to hold the ball in position. Lift the cardboard and let the ball roll.

6. Since the ball reaches maximum kinetic energy at the bottom of the ramp, measure the roll from that point to the leading edge of the ball. To more precisely define the leading edge, place the cardboard as shown.

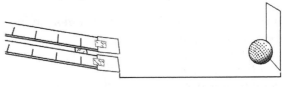

Roll measurement

7. If more than one group will be using the same ramp, have groups distinguish their butcher paper marks from each other by color-coding or other means.

8. For students ready for more independent inquiry, present the *Key Question.* Have them devise and carry out their own plans to answer the question, including variables to be controlled, data to be recorded, and the appropriate kind of graph to be constructed.

Procedure

1. Ask, "If I want the ball to roll a long way, does it matter where I put it on the ramp? How does the ball's height on the ramp affect the distance it rolls?"

2. Show the class the technique for releasing the ball (see *Management 5*). Have groups set up the ramps to a specified height and make some practice rolls to determine which ramp positions they want to test. For example, the class might decide to try every 10 centimeters from 20 to 60 (20-30-40-50-60) or every 20 centimeters from 20 to 100 (20-40-60-80-100).

3. Distribute the activity page. Have students record the type of ball, the height of ramp where it intersects the books, and the positions of the ball that will be tested.

4. Tell students to place the ball in the lowest position on the ramp, estimate how far it will roll, then perform and record three trials.

5. Have students complete the table by repeating this procedure for the other ball positions.

6. Instruct students to cross out the shortest and longest distances in each set of trials and use the remaining numbers to complete the line graph.

7. Talk about the results. Clarify that the tested variable was the ball's height from the floor (see *Connecting Learning*). A particular position on a ramp is linked to a particular height from the floor.

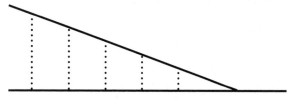

Height changes with ramp position.

8. Have students respond to the question at the bottom of the page.

Connecting Learning
1. What variables did we control? [the incline of the ramp, how the ball is released, measurement of the roll from the bottom of the ramp to the leading edge of the ball, etc.] What variable did we test? [the height of the ball from the floor]
2. What do you conclude from your results? [The higher the ball's position from the floor, the further it rolls.]
3. Why do you think this happens? [The higher the ball starts, the more potential energy it has to convert into kinetic energy.]
4. How do the heights of the ramp at the 25-cm mark and 50-cm mark compare? (Measure with the ruler perpendicular to the floor.) In which position would the ball have more potential energy? [50-cm mark]
5. Choose another position on the ramp from which to roll the ball. How can you estimate how far this ball will roll? [Determine where the starting position intersects with the line on the graph.] Try it and see if it works.
6. What does gravity have to do with the ball rolling down the ramp?
7. What are you wondering now?

* Reprinted with permission from *Principles and Standards for School Mathematics*, 2000 by the National Council of Teachers of Mathematics. All rights reserved.

Ball On a Roll

Key Question

How does the ball's height on the ramp affect the distance it rolls?

Learning Goals

Students will:

- explore how a ball's starting height on the ramp is related to the distance it rolls, and

- relate the downward movement of the ball to the force of gravity.

Ball On a Roll

How does the ball's height on the ramp affect the distance it rolls?

Type of ball:

Height of ramp:

Position of Ball (cm)	Distance of roll (cm)			
	Estimate	Trial #1	Trial #2	Trial #3

Cross out the shortest and longest distances in each set of trials. Use the remaining number (median average) for the line graph.

What did you learn?

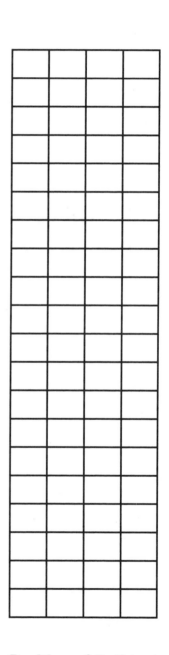

Distance of Roll (cm)

Position of Ball (cm)

Ball On a Roll

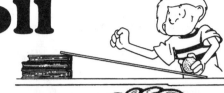

1. What variables did we control? What variables did we test?

2. What do you conclude from your results?

3. Why do you think this happens?

4. How do the heights of the ramp at the 25-cm mark and 50-cm mark compare? In which position would the ball have more potential energy?

5. Choose another position on the ramp from which to roll the ball. How can you estimate how far the ball will roll? Try it and see if it works.

6. What does gravity have to do with the ball rolling down the ramp?

7. What are you wondering now?

Catapults

Topic
Testing variables using catapults

Key Question
What can you discover about catapults?

Learning Goals
Students will:
- construct a catapult,
- experiment with accuracy and distance challenges, and
- test variables that influence how far or high a small sponge can be flung.

Guiding Documents
Project 2061 Benchmarks
- *Measuring instruments can be used to gather accurate information for making scientific comparisons of objects and events and for designing and constructing things that will work properly.*
- *Something that is moving may move steadily or change its direction. The greater the force is, the greater the change in motion will be. The more massive an object is, the less effect a given force will have.*
- *Recognize when comparisons might not be fair because some conditions are not kept the same.*

NRC Standards
- *Scientists use different kinds of investigations depending on the questions they are trying to answer. Types of investigations include describing objects, events, and organisms; classifying them; and doing a fair test (experimenting).*
- *The position and motion of objects can be changed by pushing or pulling. The size of the change is related to the strength of the push or pull.*

NCTM Standards 2000*
- *Select and apply appropriate standard units and tools to measure length, area, volume, weight, time, temperature, and the size of angles*
- *Use measures of center, focusing on the median, and understand what each does and does not indicate about the data set*

Math
Estimation
Measurement
  length
Median average
Graphing

Science
Physical science
  force and motion

Integrated Processes
Observing
Collecting and recording data
Comparing and contrasting
Identifying and controlling variables
Interpreting data
Relating

Materials
For each group:
  2" x 4" piece of wood about 8" long
    (or minimum 1" x 3 1/2" x 7")
  two 8-penny nails (2 1/2" long)
  scissors
  1 jumbo craft stick
  5 toothpicks
  glue
  1 rubber band (1/8" x 2")
  2-cm square piece of sponge
  meter stick or long meter tape

For the class:
  several hammers
  cloth-reinforced duct tape
  newspaper
  masking tape
  4 bright colors of construction paper
  chart or butcher paper
  small paper clips
  string

Background Information
Catapults provide a context for exploring variables, the focus of this activity. As students modify the catapults during the challenges, they will discover which changes or variables affect the flight of the sponge. This playful experience then leads to controlled tests. A controlled or fair test isolates one variable only; all the other variables are kept the same. Whatever changes then occur in the flight of the sponge can be attributed to how this one variable was changed. If two variables were uncontrolled, it would be difficult to determine which caused differences in the results.

Catapults also illustrate potential and kinetic energy. As the sponge is released, the potential energy stored in the stretched rubber band is transferred by the arm of the catapult to the sponge and changed to kinetic energy, the energy of motion. As students move the rubber band higher and bend the arm of the catapult against it, they will be able to feel the increased tension, the increased potential energy.

Management

1. Groups of three or four should construct and test the catapults.
2. The activity will take several days. One plan might proceed as follows:
   Day one: construct the catapults
   Day two: explore one or more challenges
   Day three: test the rubber band height variable
   Day four: test a different variable of their choosing
3. A large area, preferably indoors, will be needed to accommodate all the groups. To test the catapults, each group will need a minimal length of 6 meters. The activity can be done outdoors on a calm day.
4. Safety should be strongly emphasized, both during hammering and when using the catapults. Consider using safety goggles to protect eyes. If preferred, the nails can be hammered into each piece of wood beforehand.
5. Prepare several compass drawing tools by tying a small paper clip to each end of a piece of string so that the total length from the tip of one paper clip to the tip of the other is 30 cm. Each group can have their own or take turns using the compasses as they become available.

6. Cut 2-cm squares of construction paper in four bright colors. Each group will need 10 squares of each color.

Procedure

Constructing the catapults

Give students the construction page and the necessary materials. Have them follow the directions on the page. Do not use the catapults until the glue is completely dry, a half day or more.

Accuracy challenge

1. Distribute the challenge page. Have each group use the string compass to draw a 60-cm circle on chart paper.
2. Instruct students to cut out the circle, mark their launch line with tape or by other means, and place the center of the circle 3 meters from the launch line.

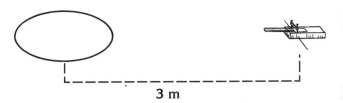

3 m

3. Tell students to experiment with their catapults until they have found a consistent way to land the sponge in the circle. Remind students that, to safely conduct a launch, group members should be clear of the launch area and be aware of when a launch is to be made.
4. Have students conduct 10 launches, record the results, and explain the launch setup (how variables were controlled).
5. Compare and contrast as a class.

Distance challenge

1. Have each group experiment with their catapult to obtain the longest distance possible, recording their launch setup and results.
2. Compare and contrast as a class.
3. Ask, "When you were doing the challenges, you tried different methods for launching. What were some of the things you changed?" [how far back the arm of the catapult was pulled, the position of the sponge along the arm, the height of the rubber band, angle of the wood base] Explain that something that can affect the results is called a variable.

Testing variables

1. Inform students that today they will be doing a controlled experiment to test one variable, how the height of the rubber band affects the distance the sponge goes.
2. Distribute the third activity page. Have students write their predictions. Tell them that the other variables will be controlled as follows: the arm of the catapult will be pulled all the way back to the board, the board will lie flat on the ground, and the sponge will be placed right behind the toothpick on top of the arm.

3. Have students make a newspaper landing path about 6 meters long by taping newspapers together and marking a starting line. Give each group 10 squares in each of four colors of construction paper and some glue. These materials plus the catapult, the sponge, and a meter stick will be taken to the launch site.

4. At the launch site, assign an area to each group. Tell each group to lay out their landing path and position the rubber band on the nails so that it rests just above the 1-cm toothpick mark on the launcher.

5. Instruct the groups to make an *x* on the landing spots of each of the 10 launches at the 1-cm height, then glue the ___ (name color) squares on these marks.

6. Ask each group to assign jobs to its members: someone to launch, someone to retrieve, someone to measure, and someone to mark the landing spot and glue the colored squares to the landing path.

7. Have the groups perform the 10 launches at the 1-cm height. Change the height of the rubber band, rotate jobs, do 10 more launches, and mark the landings with a different color. Repeat until all four heights have been tested.

8. Explain how to determine the median distance by drawing a line between the 5th and 6th squares (from the launch line) in each set of colors. Have groups measure, record, and graph the median distances.

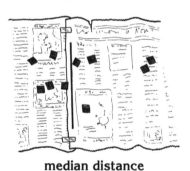

median distance

9. Discuss the results.

Connecting Learning

1. What things did you change, or experiment with, as you worked on the challenge?
2. To make a fair test, we need to control all but one variable. How did you make a fair test?
3. Describe how the sponge traveled through the air when you used lower rubber band heights compared to higher rubber band heights. [the arc gets higher as the rubber band height is increased]
4. What other things did you discover about the catapults?
5. What are you wondering now?

Extension

Encourage students to plan and test another variable such as the mass of the object being launched (various sizes of sponge or other materials) or different sizes of rubber bands.

Curriculum Correlation

Social Science

Have students research the construction and historic use of catapults. A *Project 2061 Benchmark* states: *Throughout all of history, people everywhere have invented and used tools. Most tools of today are different from those of the past but many are modifications of very ancient tools.*

* Reprinted with permission from *Principles and Standards for School Mathematics*, 2000 by the National Council of Teachers of Mathematics. All rights reserved.

Catapults

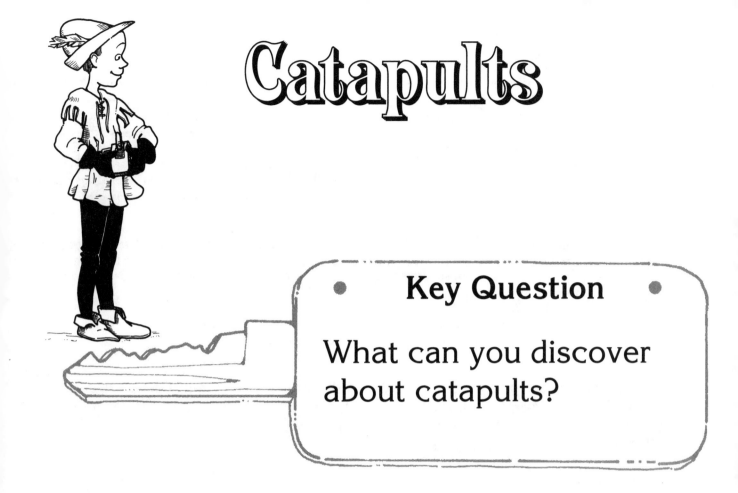

Key Question

What can you discover about catapults?

Learning Goals

Students will:

- construct a catapult,
- experiment with accuracy and distance challenges, and
- test variables that influence how far or high a small sponge can be flung.

Catapults

Construction

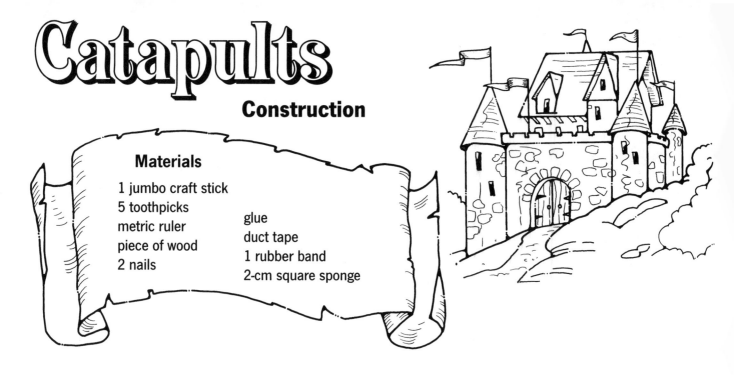

Materials

1 jumbo craft stick
5 toothpicks
metric ruler
piece of wood
2 nails

glue
duct tape
1 rubber band
2-cm square sponge

1. For the arm of the catapult, cut one tip of the craft stick to make a straight edge. Mark 1-, 2-, 3-, and 4-cm lines from this edge. Glue pieces of toothpick along each line. On the other side, glue a piece of toothpick 3 cm from the rounded tip. Let dry.

2. Draw a line across the width of the board about 6 cm from the end. Hammer two nails along this line, 6.5 cm apart.

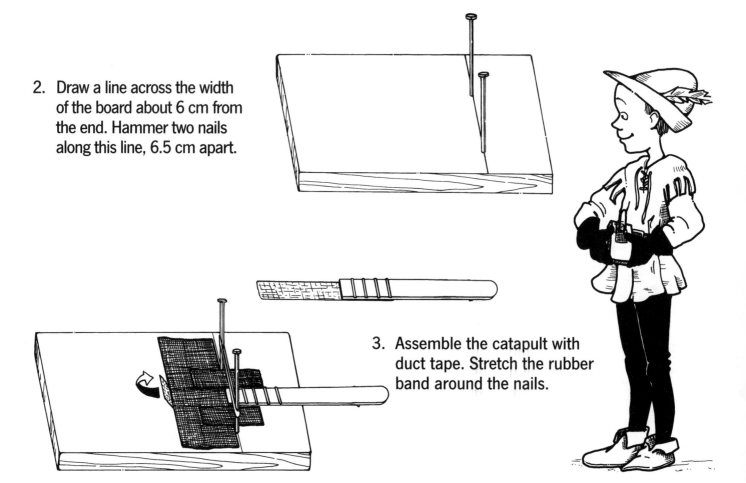

3. Assemble the catapult with duct tape. Stretch the rubber band around the nails.

Catapults

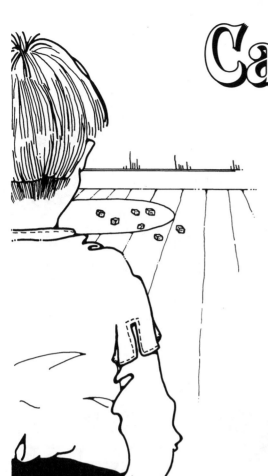

Accuracy Challenge

Consistently land the sponge in a 60-cm circle whose center is 3 meters from the catapult.

Explain your launch setup.

Of 10 launches, how many landed in the circle?

Distance Challenge

Launch the sponge as far as possible.

Explain your launch setup.

Farthest distance:

What changes did you make in trying to meet the challenges?

Catapults

How does the height of the rubber band affect the distance the sponge travels?

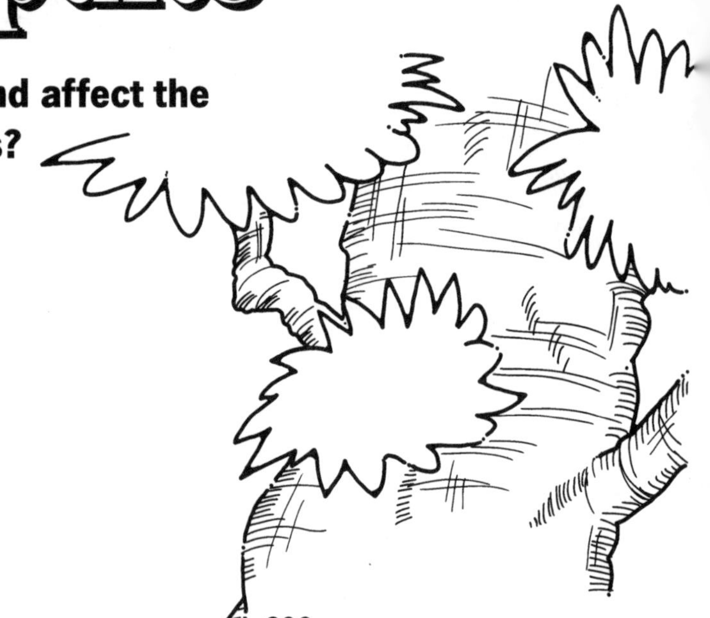

Prediction:

How will other variables be controlled?

Make 10 launches at each height.

Height of Rubber Band	Average Distance (median)*

*Measure a mark made between the 5th and 6th landings. This is the median, or middle, distance.

What did you observe?

How did your prediction compare with the results?

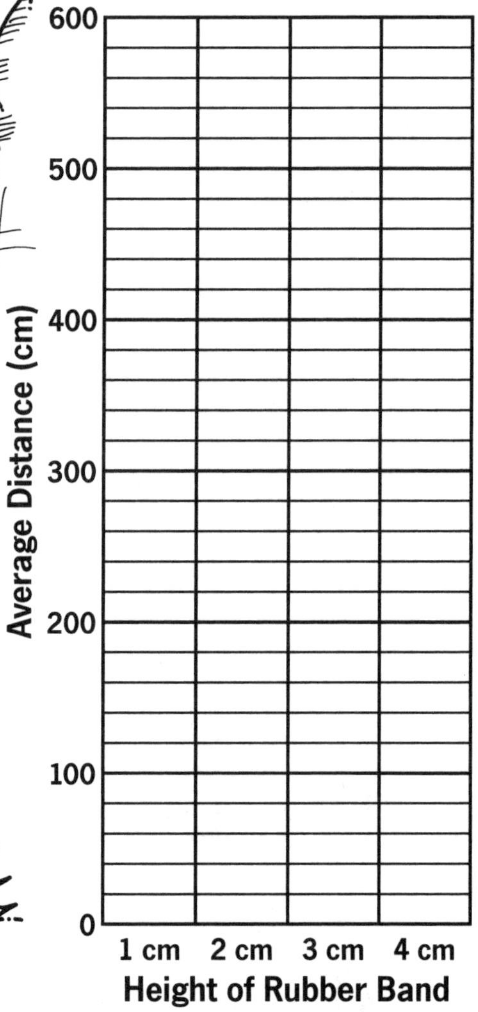

Average Distance (cm)

600
500
400
300
200
100
0

1 cm   2 cm   3 cm   4 cm
Height of Rubber Band

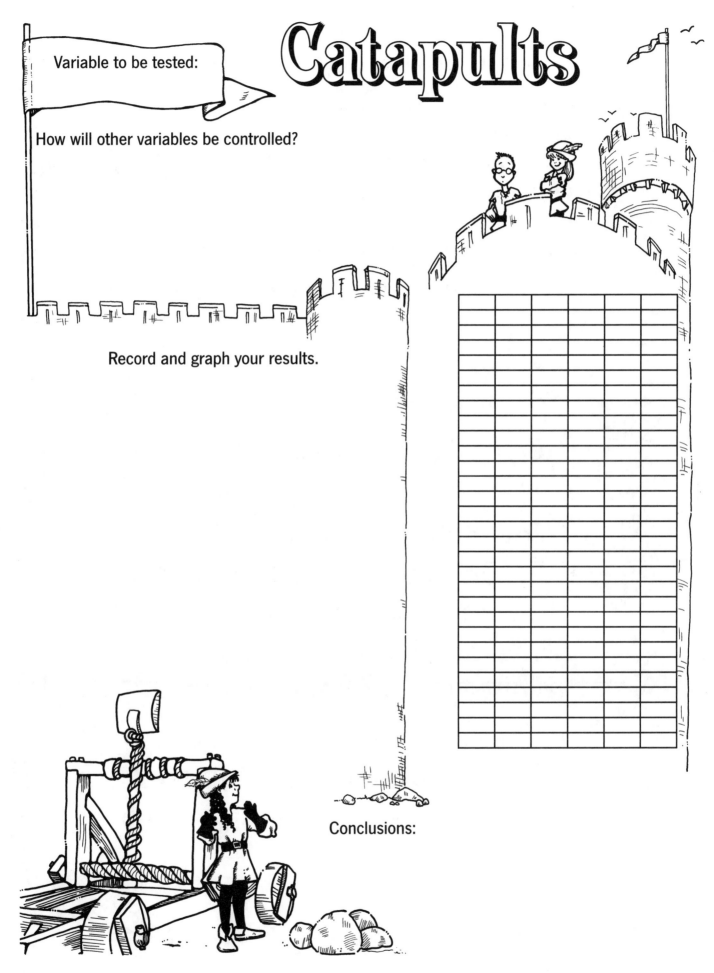

Catapults

Variable to be tested:

How will other variables be controlled?

Record and graph your results.

Conclusions:

Catapults

1. What things did you change, or experiment with, as you worked on the challenge?

2. To make a fair test, we need to control all but one variable. How did you make a fair test?

3. How did the sponge travel through the air when you used lower rubber band heights? How did that compare to using higher rubber band heights?

4. What other things did you discover about the catapults?

5. What are you wondering now?

A First-Class Job

Topic
First-class levers

Key Question
What happens when the position of the fulcrum on a first-class lever is changed?

Learning Goals
Students will:
* become familiar with the components of a first-class lever,
* investigate what happens when the fulcrum is moved, and
* discover the trade-offs of using a first-class lever.

Guiding Documents
Project 2061 Benchmarks
* *People can often learn about things around them by just observing those things carefully, but sometimes they can learn more by doing something to the things and noting what happens.*
* *People can use objects and ways of doing things to solve problems.*
* *Seeing how a model works after changes are made to it may suggest how the real thing would work if the same were done to it.*

NRC Standards
* *The position of an object can be described by locating it relative to another object or the background.*
* *The position and motion of objects can be changed by pushing or pulling. The size of the change is related to the strength of the push or pull.*

NCTM Standards 2000*
* *Select and apply appropriate standard units and tools to measure length, area, volume, weight, time, temperature, and the size of angles*
* *Propose and justify conclusions and predictions that are based on data and design studies to further investigate the conclusions or predictions.*

Mathematics
Measuring
    linear

Science
Physical science
    simple machines
        first-class levers

Integrated Processes
Observing
Predicting
Comparing and contrasting
Collecting and recording data
Interpreting data
Generalizing
Applying

Materials
2" x 6" x 8' board
Concrete block
Box filled with 10 reams of paper
2 meter sticks

Background Information
Simple machines help us do work by trading force and distance. They do NOT lessen the work because you can't get something for nothing. With simple machines, there is a trade-off, force for distance, or distance for force.

The lever is one type of simple machine. All lever systems are made up of four components: the rod, which is called the *lever*, the pivot point, which is called the *fulcrum*; the point where the *effort force* is applied; and the point where the *resistance force*, or load, is located. (*Resistance* and *load* are used interchangeably. Use the term that suits your situation.)

The *class* of the lever is determined by the center element in the arrangement of the effort, resistance, and fulcrum along the lever. In a first-class lever, the fulcrum is located between the resistance and the effort. The closer the fulcrum is to the resistance, the less effort it takes to lift it. The trade-off occurs in that the distance the resistance can be lifted is decreased. You can't get something for nothing. In this activity, students should also notice that the effort always moves in the opposite direction of the load. If they push down on the lever, the load goes up.

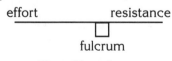

First-Class Lever

Mechanical advantage is a comparison of the resistance force (r) to the effort force (e). The ratio (r/e) informs us about the number of times the machine multiplies the force used to do the job. The term and the quantification of mechanical advantage are not introduced in this lesson; however, it is hoped that students will begin to build a conceptual understanding of the mechanical advantage of a first-class lever.

Management

1. This activity is intended for whole-class exploration.
2. Allow enough time so all students can experience the difference in the amount of effort required to lift the paper in the box with the fulcrum placed at various distances from the resistance.
3. Use proper vocabulary throughout the lesson: resistance (load), fulcrum, effort.
4. To move the fulcrum, it is easiest to pull or push on the board, leaving the concrete block in one position.

Procedure

Part One

1. Allow several students to try to lift the box of paper. (Caution them not to strain their backs; the purpose is to discover that the box is heavy.)
2. Set up the first-class lever system as illustrated. Put the box of paper on one end of the lever. With the fulcrum near the effort, let students try to lift the box of paper using the lever.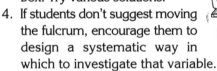
3. Ask them what they think can be done to decrease the amount of effort that is required to lift the box. Try various solutions.
4. If students don't suggest moving the fulcrum, encourage them to design a systematic way in which to investigate that variable.
5. Allow time for all students to sense the differences in the amount of effort required to lift the box with the fulcrum at various positions.
6. Ask them to make a generalization.
7. Discuss other observations such as: the resistance moved the opposite direction as our effort; when we moved the fulcrum closer to the resistance, it was easier to lift the box; we couldn't lift the box very high when the fulcrum was close to it.
8. Discuss the meaning of the following: Simple machines make a trade-off between force and distance.
9. Find other heavy objects in the classroom to lift using the lever, including adults.
10. Have students illustrate a lever that requires a great deal of force to lift the resistance. Ask them to use their own words to tell why it requires a lot of force.

Part Two

1. Inform students that they are going to do the same procedures again, but this time they will measure how high they can lift the load and how far they have to push down the effort. Ask them to discuss as a class how to organize the procedure and how to make a record of their results on their activity pages.

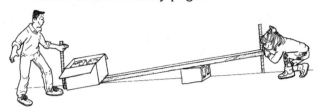

2. Follow the class plan to collect the data.
3. Direct small student groups to get together to discuss a generalization of their interpretation of the data they just collected.

Part Three

1. Inform the students that instead of them applying force to the lever to lift the paper, they will be using reams of paper to lift reams of paper.
2. Open the box of paper and take out five reams to represent the resistance. Ask a student to place them on one end of the lever. Tell the students that the other five reams will be used for the effort.

3. Ask them to predict where the fulcrum should be placed so that the five-ream effort can lift the five-ream resistance. Have them explain their reasoning. Let them try their suggestions.
4. Ask what would need to be done if only four reams of effort were used. Again ask for an explanation. Try their suggestions.
5. Follow the same procedure for three, two, and one ream of effort.

Connecting Learning

1. Why is this lever called a first-class lever? [the fulcrum is located between the effort and the resistance.]
2. Does the fulcrum have to be located halfway between the effort and the resistance in order to be a first-class lever? Explain.
3. What is the advantage of using a lever? [It allows us to use less force to lift an object.]
4. What is the cost of using less effort? [Distance, you can't lift the resistance as high.]
5. What are some real-world examples of a first-class lever?
6. When would you use a first-class lever?
7. What are you wondering now?

* Reprinted with permission from *Principles and Standards for School Mathematics, 2000* by the National Council of Teachers of Mathematics. All rights reserved.

A First-Class Job

Key Question

What happens when the position of the fulcrum on a first-class lever is changed?

Learning Goals

Students will:

- become familiar with the components of a first-class lever,
- investigate what happens when the fulcrum is moved, and
- discover the trade-offs of using a first-class lever.

A First-Class Job

Part One

Illustrate a lever that requires a lot of force to lift the box of paper.
Label the effort, fulcrum, and resistance.

Explain why this lever requires a lot of force to lift the paper.

How could you make this job easier?

52

A First-Class Job

Part Two

Make a record of the distance the paper moves and the distance the effort moves.

What conclusion(s) can you make from your data?

Part Three

Illustrate the levers that lift:

- 5 reams with 5 reams of effort

- 5 reams with 3 reams of effort

- 5 reams with 1 ream of effort

A First-Class Job

1. Why is this lever called a first-class lever?

2. Does the fulcrum have to be located halfway between the effort and the resistance in order to be a first-class lever? Explain.

3. What is the advantage of using a lever?

4. What is the cost of using less effort?

5. What are some real-world examples of a first-class lever?

6. When would you use a first-class lever?

7. What are you wondering now?

CONNECTING LEARNING

Fulcrums on the Move

Topic
First–class levers

Key Question
If you want to balance a first-class lever, what must you do when you decrease the amount of effort force?

Learning Goals
Students will:
- discover what happens when the fulcrum of a first-class lever is moved, and
- observe patterns to draw conclusions about the length of the lever arm and its load.

Guiding Documents
Project 2061 Benchmarks
- *People can often learn about things around them by just observing those things carefully, but sometimes they can learn more by doing something to the things and noting what happens.*
- *Seeing how a model works after changes are made to it may suggest how the real thing would work if the same were done to it.*
- *Tables and graphs can show how values of one quantity are related to values of another.*
- *Graphical display of numbers may make it possible to spot patterns that are not otherwise obvious, such as comparative size and trends.*

NRC Standard
- *The position of an object can be described by locating it relative to another object or the background.*

NCTM Standard 2000*
- *Use representations to model and interpret physical, social, and mathematical phenomena*

Math
Graphing
Relationships

Science
Physical science
  simple machines
  first-class levers

Integrated Processes
Observing
Predicting
Comparing and contrasting
Collecting and recording data
Interpreting data
Generalizing

Materials
Per group:
  48 Hex-a-Link™ (interlocking) cubes
  pencil
  masking tape
  2 different colored crayons or markers

Background Information
Simple machines help us do work by trading force and distance. They do NOT lessen the work because you can't get something for nothing. With simple machines, there is a trade-off, force for distance, or distance for force.

The lever is one type of simple machine. All lever systems are made up of four components: the rod, which is called the *lever;* the pivot point, which is called the *fulcrum;* the point where the *effort force* is applied; and the point where the *resistance force,* or load, is located. (*Resistance* and *load* are used interchangeably. Use the term that suits your situation.) The *class* of the lever is determined by the center element in the arrangement of the effort, resistance (load), and fulcrum along the lever.

In a first-class lever, the fulcrum is located between the resistance and the effort. The closer the fulcrum is to the resistance, the less effort it takes to lift it. The graphical representation in this activity helps students in making the generalization that when they want to use less effort force to lift an object with a first-class lever, the fulcrum needs to be moved closer to the resistance.

Management

1. This activity is intended for groups of three or four.
2. A bag of 500 Hex-a-Link™ cubes will be sufficient for a class of 35 students. Each group should have 48 cubes. It may be easier for students if 12 Hex-a-Link™ cubes of one color are used for the resistance force and 12 cubes of another color are used for the effort force.
3. Use proper vocabulary throughout the lesson: resistance (load), fulcrum, effort.
4. It is assumed students have done *A First-Class Job*.
5. To help clarify the positions on the lever, copy one set of *Lever Labels* for each group.
6. If the cubes of the lever don't hang down properly, suggest that they may need to be twisted slightly. Give students time to tinker with the setup.

Procedure

1. Allow time for students to assemble the lever system. Have them position the labels (*Resistance, Fulcrum,* and *Effort*) as indicated in the illustration.

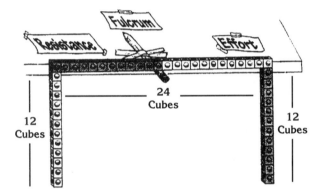

2. Review the generalizations made in the activity, *A First-Class Job*.
3. Inform the students that the resistance force will remain the same (12 Hex-a-Link™ cubes) for this entire activity.
4. Ask students where they think the fulcrum will be located to balance a resistance of 12 Hex-a-Link™ cubes with an effort force of 12 Hex-a-Link™ cubes.
5. Direct the students to *lightly* draw a line on their activity sheet to indicate their prediction for the placement of the fulcrum.
6. Allow time for them to balance the lever. Have them draw a *darker* line to indicate the actual location of the fulcrum to balance the lever. Urge them to color the resistance arm one color and the effort arm the other color.
7. Guide them to remove two Hex-a-Link™ cubes from the effort force. Have them again draw a light line to indicate their prediction of where the fulcrum will be located to balance the lever.

8. Have them test their predictions, find and record the actual results, and color in the arms of the lever using the color scheme in the previous trial.
9. Urge the students to continue the procedure, reducing the effort force by two Hex-a-Link™ cubes each time.

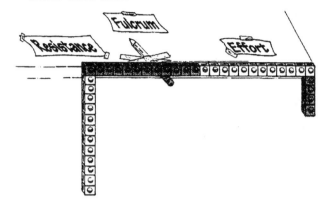

10. Ask them to write about the relationship between the number of cubes used for the effort force and the length of the effort arm.

Connecting Learning

1. What did you learn in this activity?
2. How is this activity like *A First-Class Job?*
3. What do you notice about the number of cubes on the resistance side of your graph? [The number of cubes stays the same.]
4. What do you notice about the number of cubes on the effort side of your graph? [The number of cubes gets smaller.]
5. What do you notice about the lengths of the bars of the effort side of your graph as the number of cubes gets smaller? [The lengths of the bars get longer.] Explain.
6. When using a first-class lever, what do we have to do to use less effort to lift something? Explain how your data record supports this.
7. Did any of your data surprise you? Explain.
8. What are you wondering now?

* Reprinted with permission from *Principles and Standards for School Mathematics, 2000* by the National Council of Teachers of Mathematics. All rights reserved.

Fulcrums on the Move

Key Question

If you want to balance a first-class lever, what must you do when you decrease the amount of effort force?

Learning Goals

Students will:

- discover what happens when the fulcrum of a first-class lever is moved, and
- draw conclusions from patterns about the length of the lever arm and its load.

Lever Labels

Each square represents one cube. Draw a line to indicate the position of the fulcrum that balances the system. Color the cubes of the resistance arm one color and the cubes of the effort arm another color.

Resistance   **Effort**

12 [grid of squares] 12

Describe the fulcrum's position:

12 [grid of squares] 10

Describe the fulcrum's position:

12 [grid of squares] 8

Describe the fulcrum's position:

12 [grid of squares] 6

Describe the fulcrum's position:

12 [grid of squares] 4

Describe the fulcrum's position:

12 [grid of squares] 2

Describe the fulcrum's position:

On the back side of this paper, write what you know about the position of the fulcrum and the amount of effort needed to balance the lever.

Fulcrums on the Move

1. What did you learn in this activity?

2. How is this activity like *A First-Class Job?*

3. What do you notice about the number of cubes on the resistance side of your graph?

4. What do you notice about the number of cubes on the effort side of your graph?

5. What do you notice about the lengths of the bars of the effort side of your graph as the number of cubes gets smaller? Explain.

6. When using a first-class lever, what do we have to do to use less effort to lift something? Explain how your data record supports this.

7. Did any of your data surprise you? Explain.

8. What are you wondering now?

Level the Lever

Topic
First-class lever

Key Question
How can you balance a first-class lever?

Learning Goal
Students will discover the mathematical pattern for balancing a first-class lever.

Guiding Documents
Project 2061 Benchmarks
- *Mathematical ideas can be represented concretely, graphically, and symbolically.*
- *Measuring instruments can be used to gather accurate information for making scientific comparisons of objects and events and for designing and constructing things that will work properly.*

NRC Standard
- *The position of an object can be described by locating it relative to another object or the background.*

NCTM Standards 2000*
- *Solve problems that arise in mathematics and in other contexts*
- *Model problem situations with objects and use representations such as graphs, tables, and equations to draw conclusions*

Math
Patterns
Measurement
Estimation
Computation
   multiplication and addition
Problem solving

Science
Physical science
   simple machines
      first-class lever

Integrated Processes
Observing
Predicting
Comparing and contrasting
Collecting and recording data
Interpreting data
Generalizing
Applying

Materials
Per group:
   1 50-cm wooden strip (see *Management 1*)
   2 medium binder clips
   pencil
   tape
   distance measurer, included
   clay, optional (see *Management 3*)
   Unifix® cubes or Hex-a-Link™ cubes

Background Information
The scientific formula for determining work is force times distance ($W = f \times d$). Simple machines help us do work by trading force for distance. They do NOT lessen the work; there is a trade-off, force for distance.

The lever is one type of simple machine. All lever systems are made up of four components: the rod, which is called the *lever*; the pivot point, which is called the *fulcrum*; the point where the *effort force* is applied; and the point where the *resistance force*, or load, is located. The *class* of the lever is determined by the center element in the arrangement of the effort, resistance, and fulcrum along the lever. In a first-class lever, the fulcrum is located between the resistance and the effort. A familiar example is a seesaw.

In order to balance a first-class lever, the forces (resistance and effort) on either side of the fulcrum must be evenly distributed. This means that the force times the distance on one side of the fulcrum must equal the force times the distance on the other side. (Non-customary measuring units will be used in this activity, Unifix® cubes and corresponding distance units.)

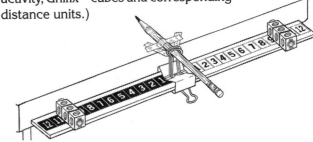

Resistance Side
3 Unifix® cubes
Distance from fulcrum
  = 10 distance units

Effort Side
3 Unifix® cubes
Distance from fulcrum
  = 10 distance units

$$3 \times 10 = 3 \times 10$$

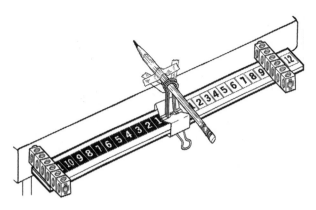

Resistance Side
6 Unifix® cubes
Distance from fulcrum

= 10 distance units

Effort Side
6 Unifix® cubes
Distance from fulcrum
= 12 distance units

and 1 Unifix® cube
at 12 distance units

$$6 \times 12 = (6 \times 10) + (1 \times 12)$$

In both examples, the force times the distance on the resistance side of the fulcrum equals the force times the distance on the effort side of the fulcrum. The lever system is therefore balanced!

Management

1. Options for the wooden strips:
   - Purchase lattice strips or laths from lumber supplies.
   - Spacer strips are often free for the asking from lumber supplies. These are the wooden strips placed between larger boards to allow for air circulation. They are quite rough and will need to be cut and sanded. To engage students in the preparation of materials, an area can be set up a couple of days ahead of time where students saw the spacer strips to the appropriate length and then sand their surfaces.
   - Rip a 2" x 4" board into pieces approximately 2" wide x 1/4" deep x 22 1/4" long. Students in high school Industrial Technology classes may be willing to do this for you.
   - Wooden meter sticks can be cut in half.
2. Copy the included distance measurer onto colored paper. Laminate, if possible, to help preserve them.
3. Students should not spend a great deal of time with the initial balancing of their levers. Clay or paper clips can be used to balance them, but they must remain in place for the entire activity.
4. Assemble a lever system beforehand so that students can use the model for their constructions.
   a. Cut out the distance measurer. Tape it together so that the dark side and light side meet and measure out from the center.

`12 11 10 9 8 7 6 5 4 3 2 1 0 1 2 3 4 5 6 7 8 9 10 11 12`

b. Tape the distance measurer on top of the wooden strip.
c. Attach two binder clips to the center of the lever over the zero on the distance measurer.
d. Use tape to secure a pencil to the table or desk. Make sure the eraser end of the pencil extends over the edge.
e. Hang the lever on the pencil end using the loops of the binder clips. If necessary, balance the lever with pieces of clay or paper clips.

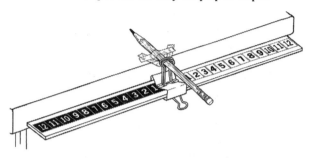

5. Have students work in groups of four.
6. For the sake of consistency, have students place the Unifix® cubes so they are centered over the measuring marks. The Unifix® cube trains should be placed perpendicular to the distance measurer; vertically placed Unifix® cube trains will easily topple when the lever is not balanced.
7. If appropriate for your students, use the terms *effort force*, *effort arm*, *resistance force*, and *resistance arm*. (*Resistance* and *load* are interchangeable terms. Use the term that fits your situation.)

Procedure

1. Ask the *Key Question*.
2. Allow time for students to assemble their lever systems. Have the students make certain the levers are level (balanced).
3. Distribute Unifix® cubes. Ask students to place one Unifix® cube on the 10 distance mark on the dark side of the measuring tape. Discuss what happens to the lever.
4. Ask students how they could "Level the Lever." Give them some free exploration time to work at leveling the lever with various groupings of Unifix® cubes.
5. Invite students to share what they have discovered.
6. Distribute the first two activity pages. Urge students to apply what they have learned in their free exploration time to the tasks on the page. Encourage them to guess and test. If their predictions don't match the actual results, have them continue to work at the tasks until they begin to see the relationship of force times distance.
7. Once students understand the relationship, have them make up several situations to challenge other groups using the activity sheet *Designing Your*

Own Work. For example: On one side of the lever, 3 Unifix® cubes at 10 distance units and 2 Unifix® cubes at 12 distance units.

Establish the rule that the other groups cannot duplicate the scenario on the opposite side of the lever; they must use a different combination of force and distance units. (The other groups may choose to place 4 Unifix® cubes at 10 cm or 2 Unifix® cubes at 7 cm.)

The students will cut out and glue the *Cube Patterns* on top of the lever's illustrated distance measures. The group that is solving the problems will also cut out and glue the *Cube Patterns* on the opposite arm of the illustrated lever.

8. Once the groups have solved each other's scenarios, ask them to share results with the entire class. Urge students to use their multiplication skills to determine if the various solutions will work, then try them out to verify.

9. Have students generalize the pattern for balancing the lever. [force times distance on one side must equal force times distance on the other side]

Connecting Learning

1. How did you determine whether the lever was balanced?
2. When did you notice there was a pattern to the numbers that you could use to balance the lever?
3. What pattern did you discover?
4. Did anyone try other patterns that you later found wouldn't apply to all situations? If so, what were they? Why didn't they work?
5. How does what you learned in this activity apply to balancing a seesaw?
6. What was your favorite solution to another group's problem? Why did you like it?
7. What are you wondering now?

Extensions

1. Use one object of known weight and balance an object of an unknown weight on the lever. Challenge students to determine the unknown weight.
2. Use LEGO® pieces to do *Beams Over Board* from the AIMS publication, *Brick Layers*.
3. Apply the lesson of the first-class lever to mobiles. Do *Hanging in the Balance* (*AIMS®*, Volume IX, Number 10).

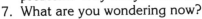
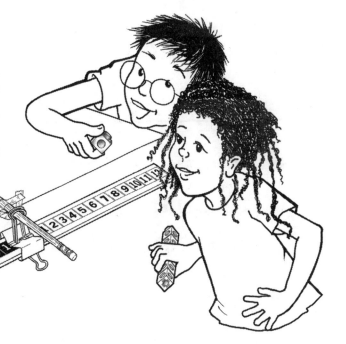

Level the Lever

Key Question

How can you balance a first-class lever?

Learning Goal

Students will:

- discover the mathematical pattern for balancing a first-class lever.

Level the Lever

the

Distance Measurer

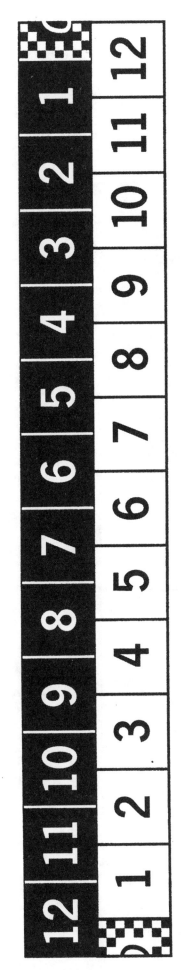

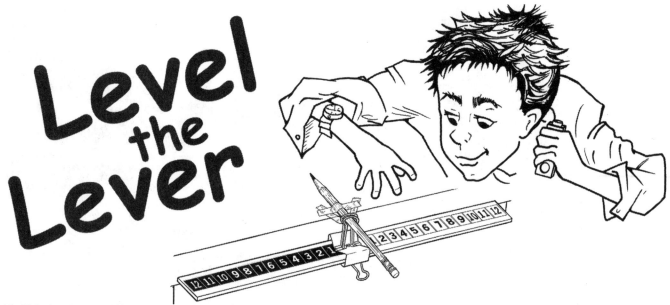

Level the Lever

Build the lever. Place the number of cubes at the distance shown in the table. Balance the lever by placing cubes on the other side of the lever. Record the distance.

Number of Cubes	Distance Units	Number of Cubes	Distance Units
1	10	1	
1	10	2	
1	6	1	
1	6	2	
1	6	3	
1	12	1	
1	12	2	
1	12	3	
1	12	4	

Tell two more ways to balance one cube at distance 12.

How can you balance two cubes at distance 10?

Write two number sentences to show that you understand the pattern that balances the lever.

Now solve these problems.

Number of Cubes	Distance Units	Number of Cubes	Distance Units
2	8		4
3	8		6
3	8		3
4	9	3	
6	4		2
4	6	2	
4	5		10
1 2	6 8	2	
2 2	5 7	3	
	3	2 2	5 7
4		2 2	3 11
		1 2	5 10

Designing Your Own Work

Design your own lever-balancing problems for another group to solve.

| 12 | 11 | 10 | 9 | 8 | 7 | 6 | 5 | 4 | 3 | 2 | 1 | | 1 | 2 | 3 | 4 | 5 | 6 | 7 | 8 | 9 | 10 | 11 | 12 |

| 12 | 11 | 10 | 9 | 8 | 7 | 6 | 5 | 4 | 3 | 2 | 1 | | 1 | 2 | 3 | 4 | 5 | 6 | 7 | 8 | 9 | 10 | 11 | 12 |

| 12 | 11 | 10 | 9 | 8 | 7 | 6 | 5 | 4 | 3 | 2 | 1 | | 1 | 2 | 3 | 4 | 5 | 6 | 7 | 8 | 9 | 10 | 11 | 12 |

| 12 | 11 | 10 | 9 | 8 | 7 | 6 | 5 | 4 | 3 | 2 | 1 | | 1 | 2 | 3 | 4 | 5 | 6 | 7 | 8 | 9 | 10 | 11 | 12 |

Cube Patterns

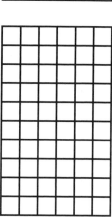

Level the Lever

- Cut out some cubes from the pattern below.

- Arrange and glue them on the dark side of each of the four levers.

- Trade papers with another group.

- Cut out and glue cube patterns to the light side of the levers to balance them.

- Write the number sentences that balance the levers.

Level the Lever

Connecting Learning

1. How did you determine whether the lever was balanced?

2. When did you notice there was a pattern to the numbers that you could use to balance the lever?

3. What pattern did you discover?

4. Did anyone try other patterns that you later found wouldn't apply to all situations? If so, what were they? Why didn't they work?

5. How does what you learned in this activity apply to balancing a seesaw?

6. What was your favorite solution to another group's problem? Why did you like it?

Brick Slide

Topic
Friction

Key Question
How easily can you pull a brick across different surfaces?

Learning Goal
Students will compare—first by sensing and then by measuring—the amount of friction produced by various surfaces.

Guiding Documents
Project 2061 Benchmark
"Students should have lots of experiences to shape their intuition about motion and forces long before encountering laws. Especially helpful are experimentation and discussion of what happens as surfaces become more elastic or more free of friction." (pg. 88)

NRC Standards
* *The position and motion of objects can be changed by pushing or pulling. The size of the change is related to the strength of the push or pull.*
* *Science and technology have been practiced by people for a long time.*

NCTM Standard 2000*
* *Understand how to measure using nonstandard and standard units*

Math
Measurement
    non-customary length
Ordering

Science
Physical science
    force and motion
        friction

Social Science
History
    Egypt

Integrated Processes
Observing
Predicting
Collecting and recording data
Comparing and contrasting
Interpreting data

Materials
For each group:
    brick, approx. 8" x 3 1/2" x 2 1/2"
    4 cm x 43 cm cardboard strip
    #84 rubber band (1/2" x 3 1/2")
    160 cm medium- or heavy-weight string
    2 regular paper clips
    scissors
    glue
    crayons or colored pencils
    hand lenses

For the class:
    a picture of an Egyptian pyramid
    hole punch

Background Information
Friction
   A force is a push or a pull. Friction is a force, a resistance to motion. As an object moves in one direction, friction pushes against it in the opposite direction. Whenever two surfaces rub against each other, there is *sliding friction*. Children and adults have experienced it going down slides on the playground, sliding a book across a desk, moving a chair across the floor, gliding across the ice on skates, and in countless other ways.

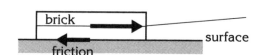

   The amount of sliding friction depends on the kinds of surfaces and the weight of an object. Since only one object, a brick, is being tested here, the weight remains the same. The manipulated variable is the kind of surface. Rough surfaces tend to have higher friction than smooth surfaces, but no surface is completely free of friction.
   Sometimes a lot of friction is desirable. Rubber, a high-friction material, is used on the soles of basketball shoes so players can stop quickly without sliding.

Other times, low-friction materials, such as smooth metals, are better. They make it easier to go down a slide or skate across the ice. Sharpening smooths the nicks in ice skate blades, reducing friction.

As students do this activity, they should also notice the contrast between *starting friction* and *sliding friction*. It takes more force to start the brick in motion than to keep it in motion.

Egyptian pyramids

The pyramids in Egypt were built as tombs for the pharaohs. They are some of the longest-lasting human-made structures in the world. The early pyramids, built around 2600 BC, were made of huge blocks of limestone from quarries near present-day Cairo. These blocks, with an average estimated weight of about 2250 kilograms (2.5 tons), were hauled on wooden sleds over a path of logs to the river. The blocks were then loaded onto barges that traveled down the river to the building site.

The Great Pyramid at Giza, built for Cheops, is composed of over 2,000,000 blocks. Its base was almost a perfect square, about 230 meters (251.5 yards) on each side. It is the largest and oldest of the pyramids.

Management

1. The Egyptians had to haul their blocks out of the rock quarries and over various outdoor terrain. To simulate these conditions, take a survey of the possible surfaces available on your school grounds such as concrete, grass, asphalt, dirt, wood (perhaps on a table), sand, linoleum, etc. A length of about 1.5 meters will be needed at each surface site.
2. Tie string around each brick's perimeter and attach a pulling string about 70 cm long. The pulling string will later be used on the rubber band scale.
3. All students should do the qualitative investigation. You are encouraged to continue with the quantitative investigation to confirm or alter initial conclusions.
4. Before doing the quantitative investigation, have students construct the rubber band scales using the directions on the provided page.
5. The rubber band scale is not calibrated to any unit of force such as newtons. It is an informal way to make comparisons that may be difficult to judge qualitatively.

   Variations in rubber bands mean that quantitative comparisons between groups may or may not be valid. Each group should use their own scale to test all surfaces.
6. Divide the class into five groups, one for each surface to be tested.

Procedure

Part One: A Qualitative Investigation

1. Show the class a picture of an Egyptian pyramid. Explain that the Egyptians had to haul the rock blocks, weighing around 2250 kilograms or 2.5 tons, to the building site. (Don't reveal how this was done.) "I wonder what it would be like to drag those blocks over different kinds of ground. Today we are going to try it using bricks."
2. Identify the three to five surfaces that will be tested and their locations, preferably not too far apart.
3. Explain that one person from each group will pull a brick over all the chosen surfaces and, by feeling the amount of pull needed, order the surfaces from easiest pull to hardest pull on a piece of scratch paper. Repeat for each person in the group.
4. Informally, ask the class to predict the surfaces with the easiest and hardest pulls.
5. Instruct each group to get a brick with a pulling string attached and perform the investigation.
6. Share and discuss the ordering.

Part Two: A Quantitative Investigation

1. Tell the class that measuring the force of the pull is a good way to test the order of the surfaces they have recorded.
2. Give each group the two activity pages that they will need to tape or glue together. In each of the designated areas, have them write the names of the surfaces to be tested. Explain that the remaining space is for descriptive words, a rubbing, and/or drawing of the surface.
3. Instruct each group to collect a rubber band scale, previously assembled, and brick. Demonstrate how to use the scale. Measure the pull after the brick is in motion, not the stronger initial pull (starting friction).
4. Caution students to take several readings of the length of the stretch for each surface and record the most common or most repeated measurement (mode) in the trees. Measuring while in motion is, by its nature, approximate.
5. Have students use hand lenses to carefully examine the surface, then record descriptive words (hard/soft, rough/smooth, etc.), make a crayon rubbing, or draw a picture of the surface.
6. Assemble back in the classroom to examine the data. Ask students to order the surfaces from easiest pull to hardest pull.
7. Have students compare the quantitative results with the qualitative results.
8. Suggest they study their surface descriptions to see if any generalizations can be made and answer the question at the bottom of the page.

Connecting Learning

Part One

1. How did it feel pulling the brick across different surfaces?
2. On which surfaces did the brick pull the easiest? ...pull the hardest?
3. What new questions do you have?

Part Two

1. As you pulled on the brick, did you notice any changes in your rubber band readings? How did it feel? [It was more difficult at first (starting friction). Once the brick started sliding, it became easier (sliding friction).]
2. Which surface took the least amount of force to move the brick? Which took the greatest amount of force?
3. What else did you notice? [Some surfaces, such as sand or grass, may shift or pile up as objects move across them.]
4. How might you describe the surfaces that had the least friction? [hard, smooth] How would you describe the surface of the brick? [somewhat rough]
5. What different surfaces are on the seats of chairs? [fabric, leather, wood, plastic, etc.] On which ones would you slide most easily?
6. Rolling friction can be related to sliding friction. Describe your experiences riding a bicycle on different surfaces. How do they relate to our brick test? [Hard, relatively smooth surfaces are easier to ride on than something like sand or grass.]
7. If you wanted to have less friction, what surfaces might you try to slide over each other? [a cookie sheet, an ice cube, the flat side of a glass bottle, etc.]
8. What are you wondering now?

Curriculum Correlation

Literature

Jeunesse, Gallimard, Claude Delafosse, and Philippe Biard. *Pyramids*. Scholastic (A First Discovery Book). New York. 1995. (A very visual, introductory book on the pyramids.)

Macaulay, David. *Pyramid*. Houghton Mifflin. Boston. 1975.

Brick Slide

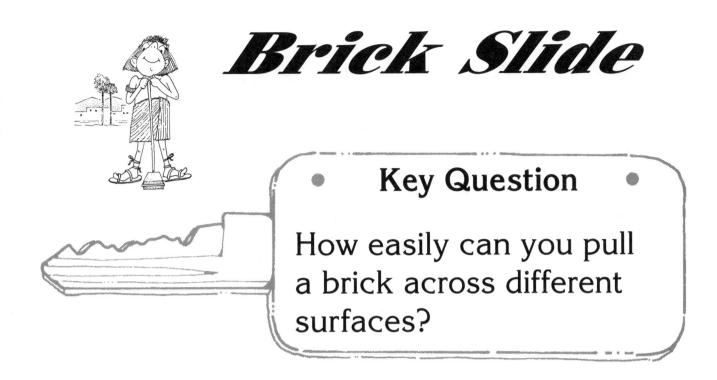

Key Question

How easily can you pull a brick across different surfaces?

Learning Goal

Students will:

- compare—first by sensing and then by measuring—the amount of friction produced by various surfaces.

Brick Slide

Rubber Band Scale

Materials
4 cm x 43 cm cardboard strip
#84 rubber band (1/2" x 3 1/2")
160 cm of string
2 paper clips
Scissors
Glue

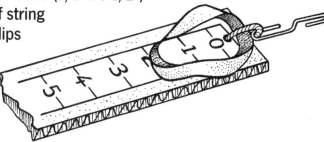

Constructing the scale

1. Cut the glue the numbered strips to make one long scale. Glue onto the center of the cardboard.
2. Punch holes at the top and bottom.
3. Attach the rubber band by threading a small piece of string through the hole and tying it.
4. Open a paper clip and hook one end onto the string.
5. Tie about 70 cm of string to the bottom of the rubber band. Thread it through a paper clip inserted in the bottom hole. Leave the string loose.

Using the Scale

1. Tie the remaining string around the brick's perimeter.
2. Hook the top of the scale onto the brick's string.
3. To move the brick across a surface, pull on the string below the paper clip.
4. Once it is in motion, measure the force. Measure several times and record the most repeated measurement for each surface.

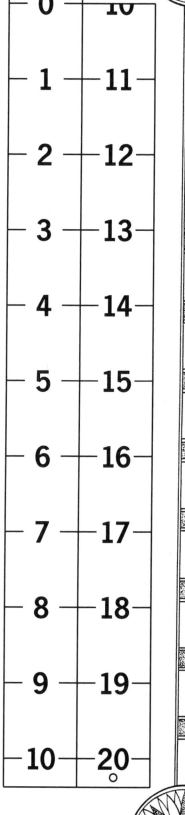

0   10
1   11
2   12
3   13
4   14
5   15
6   16
7   17
8   18
9   19
10   20

Brick Slide

How easily can a brick be pulled across different surfaces?

Use words, rubbings, and/or pictures to describe the surface. Record the measurement in the tree.

It's 2600 BC and you are building a pyramid in Egypt. You need to pull huge blocks of rock from the quarry to the building site. You are going to use a brick to test the job ahead of you.

Length of stretch:

Surface:

Length of stretch:

Surface:

Length of stretch:

Surface:

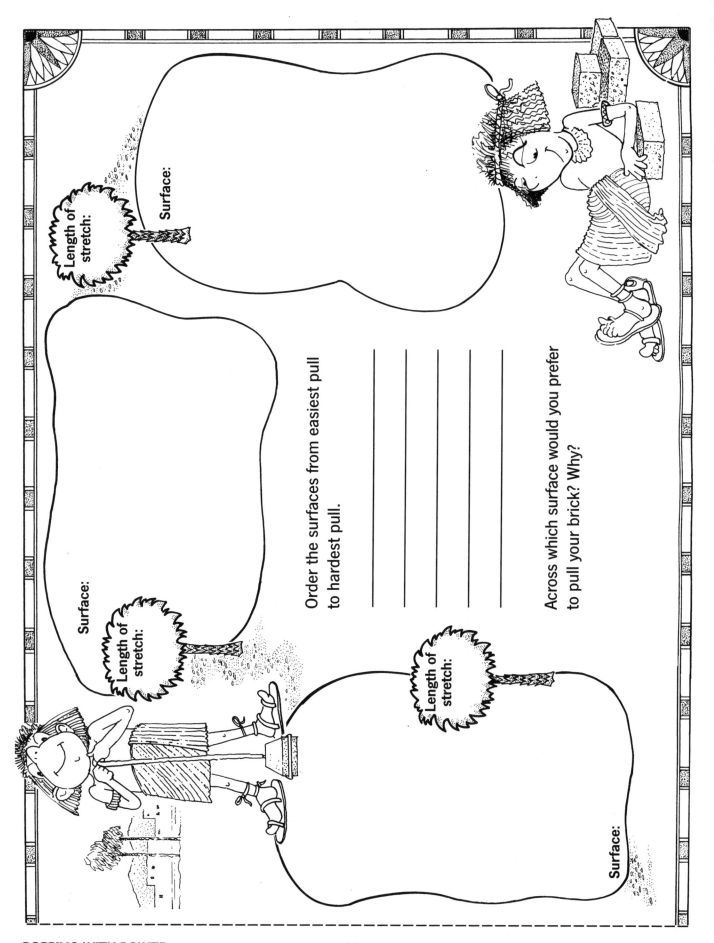

Length of stretch:

Surface:

Surface:

Length of stretch:

Order the surfaces from easiest pull to hardest pull.

_____
_____
_____
_____
_____

Across which surface would you prefer to pull your brick? Why?

Length of stretch:

Surface:

Brick Slide

Part One

1. How did it feel pulling the brick across different surfaces?

2. On which surfaces did the brick pull the easiest? ...the hardest?

3. What new questions do you have?

Part Two

1. As you pulled on the brick, did you notice any changes in your rubber band readings? How did it feel?

2. Which surface took the least amount of force to move the brick? Which took the greatest amount of force?

3. What else did you notice?

4. How might you describe the surfaces that had the least friction? How would you describe the surface of the brick?

5. What different surfaces are on the seats of chairs? On which ones would you slide most easily?

6. *Rolling friction* can be related to *sliding friction*. Describe your experiences riding a bicycle on different surfaces. How do they relate to our brick test?

7. If you wanted less friction, what surfaces might you try to slide over each other?

8. What are you wondering now?

Science on the Slide

Topic
Friction

Key Question
Which objects will go the farthest on the playground slide?

Learning Goals
Students will:
- explore the force of friction, and
- learn two methods of reducing friction.

Guiding Documents
Project 2061 Benchmarks
"Students should have lots of experiences to shape their intuition about motion and forces long before encountering laws. Especially helpful are experimentation and discussion of what happens as surfaces become more elastic or more free of friction." (pg. 88)
- *People can often learn about things around them by just observing those things carefully, but sometimes they can learn more by doing something to the things and noting what happens.*
- *Raise questions about the world around them and be willing to seek answers to some of them by making careful observations and trying things out.*

NRC Standard
- *An object's motion can be described by tracing and measuring its position over time.*

NCTM Standards 2000*
- *Select and apply appropriate standard units and tools to measure length, area, volume, weight, time, temperature, and the size of angles*
- *Collect data using observations, surveys, and experiments*
- *Represent data using tables and graphs such as line plots, bar graphs, and line graphs*

Math
Measurement
  length
Graph
  bar

Science
Physical science
  force and motion
    friction

Integrated Processes
Observing
Predicting
Collecting and recording data
Comparing and contrasting
Interpreting data
Relating

Materials
For each pair of students:
  small classroom object (see *Management 1*)
  2 meters of adding machine tape

For the class:
  playground slide
  chalk
  2 meters of yarn
  meter tape (see *Management 4*)
  1 pair of scissors
  chalkboard eraser and clay
    (see *Connecting Learning 9*)

Background Information
Friction is a force that resists motion and slows things down. It is caused by the irregularities in the surfaces of materials. Every surface has bumps and hollows so that when two surfaces are rubbed together, the bumps and hollows catch and stick to resist the movement of the surfaces over each other. Smooth surfaces produce less friction than rough surfaces. Friction can be reduced by changing the shape of an object (rolling the flattened piece of clay into a ball) so that less surface area comes in contact with the other object or by using lubricants such as oil to fill in the spaces and make the surface smoother.

Sometimes friction can be useful. We could not walk without friction because our feet would slip. We could not hold a pen or pencil. Automobile brakes use friction to slow down a moving car. Friction helps hold nails and screws in wood.

Management
1. Each pair of students needs a different small object, one that fits in the palm of their hand.
2. Fold back ten centimeters of each adding machine tape strip. Students will use this end to illustrate the object they are testing.

fold line

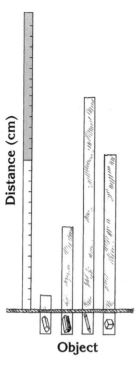

Object

Procedure

1. Have each pair of students choose an object they want to test. Explain that they will be observing the distances the objects shoot off the playground slide and determining which properties cause the objects to travel far or not so far.

2. Distribute the adding machine tape. Have each student pair draw the illustration of their chosen object on the folded 10-cm end of the tape.

3. Ask students, one at a time, to hold up the objects they have selected. After viewing all of them, give students the activity page and have each one record his or her prediction about which object will go the farthest. Allow time for them to discuss why they predicted as they did.

4. Outside, mark the starting height by making a horizontal chalk line about half way up the slide, taking into account the heights of your students.

5. Have one student from each pair release (not push) their object from the starting line. Have the other student measure the distance the object shot off the slide by placing the fold line of the adding machine tape at the bottom edge of the slide and cutting the other end where the leading edge of the object lands. Repeat until all pairs have tested their objects.

6. Return to the classroom. Tell each pair to put their adding machine tape alongside the meter tapes on the graph, record this measure on their tape, and add their tape to the graph.

7. Discuss the results on the graph. Have students compare and contrast the properties of the objects that went the farthest and those that went the least distance.

3. Each student pair will cut the tape to indicate the distance from the end of the slide to where their object lands. This strip will become part of the class bar graph.

4. Prior to doing the activity, copy and assemble two meter tapes from the back of this book. Use different colors so students can readily see where one meter ends and the next one begins.

5. Construct the frame of the class bar graph, with the meter tape forming the vertical axis and the yarn forming the horizontal axis.

8. Ask students to brainstorm what could be done to those objects that did not go far to make them go further. If necessary, guide the discussion to include changing the shape of the object or adding a lubricant.

   Have students devise and implement several plans to see if the objects actually go farther.

9. Discuss instances when friction is advantageous and when it is not.

Connecting Learning

1. What did you notice about the objects that went a far distance off the slide? [smooth surfaces, round shapes, little surface area in contact with the slide, etc.]

2. For what types of things would you want these same properties? [roller blades, certain toys that need to move freely, heavy things that need to be moved]

3. What properties did you observe in those objects that did not go far? [rough surfaces, a lot of surface area in contact with the slide, etc.]

4. For what types of things would you want these same properties? [basketball shoes, brakes on a bicycle, etc.]

5. What can be done to objects to reduce the friction between the object and the surface? [change the shape or position so there is less area in contact, lubricate the surface]

6. Which three objects traveled the farthest? How do you know? [These objects have longer strips of adding machine tape on the graph.]

7. If we were to rank the objects we tested from least distance traveled to greatest distance traveled, what would the order be? How does this relate to the force of friction?

8. How did your prediction compare to the actual results? What do you now know that would help you predict the objects that would go the farthest?

9. What could I do to get a chalkboard eraser and a flattened piece of clay to shoot off the slide the same distance? [roll clay into a ball; use lubricants, wax paper, etc. to reduce friction]

10. What are you wondering now?

* Reprinted with permission from *Principles and Standards for School Mathematics,* 2000 by the National Council of Teachers of Mathematics. All rights reserved.

Science on the Slide

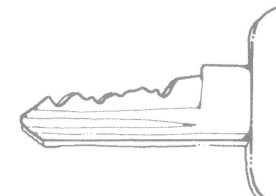

Key Question

Which objects will go the farthest on the playground slide?

Learning Goals

Students will:

- explore the force of friction, and
- learn two methods of reducing friction.

Science on the Slide

Which objects will go the farthest on the playground slide?

Prediction

Which three objects went the farthest?

How are these objects alike?

What can you do to the other objects to make them go farther?

Make a plan and try it out.

Science on the Slide

1. What did you notice about the objects that went a far distance off the slide?

2. For what types of things would you want these same properties?

3. What properties did you observe in those objects that did not go far?

4. For what types of things would you want these same properties?

5. What can be done to objects to reduce the friction between the object and the surface?

6. Which three objects traveled the farthest? How do you know?

7. If we were to rank the objects we tested from least distance traveled to greatest distance traveled, what would the order be? How does this relate to the force of friction?

8. How did your prediction compare to the actual results? What do you now know that would help you predict the objects that would go the farthest?

9. What could I do to get a chalkboard eraser and a flattened piece of clay to shoot off the slide the same distance?

10. What are you wondering now?

Slip, Sliding Away

Topic
Friction

Key Question
How can we reduce friction?

Learning Goal
Students will compare how effective several lubricants are in reducing friction.

Guiding Documents
Project 2061 Benchmark
"Students should have lots of experiences to shape their intuition about motion and forces long before encountering laws. Especially helpful are experimentation and discussion of what happens as surfaces become more elastic or more free of friction." (page 88)

NRC Standards
- *The position and motion of objects can be changed by pushing or pulling. The size of the change is related to the strength of the push or pull.*
- *The motion of an object can be described by its position, direction of motion, and speed. That motion can be measured and represented on a graph.*

NCTM Standards 2000*
- *Select and apply appropriate standard units and tools to measure length, area, volume, weight, time, temperature, and the size of angles*
- *Use measures of center, focusing on the median, and understand what each does and does not indicate about the data set*

Math
Measurement
   length
   mass
   time (digital)
Decimals
Median average
Bar graph
Ordering

Science
Physical science
   force and motion
      friction

Integrated Processes
Observing
Controlling variables
Collecting and recording data
Comparing and contrasting
Interpreting data
Relating

Materials
For the class:
   meter sticks or measuring tapes
   balance and gram masses
   paper/cloth towels, liquid soap, and water for cleanup

For each group:
   desk or table (see *Management 1*)
   books or other props (see *Management* 1)
   film canister filled with sand
   lubricants such as soap, wax, and oil
     (see *Management 4*)
   small piece of sponge (see *Management 5*)
   corrugated cardboard, 15 cm x 6 cm
   masking tape
   stopwatch
   colored pencils

Background Information
   A force is a push or pull. *Friction is a force, a resistance to motion.* As an object moves in one direction due to gravity or another force, friction pushes against it in the opposite direction. Whenever two surfaces rub against each other, there is sliding friction. This is not only true for solid against solid but also for solid against gas such as air. Think of a parachute where air resistance (friction) is needed to slow the descent or of an aerodynamic car where friction between air and car has been reduced, increasing fuel efficiency.

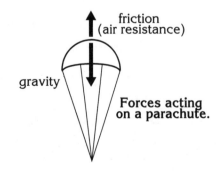

friction
(air resistance)

gravity

**Forces acting
on a parachute.**

The amount of friction varies with the kind of surface. Smooth surfaces tend to create less friction than rough surfaces. However, even the smoothest surfaces have slight imperfections that cause friction.

The amount of friction also varies with the force (weight) pressing the surfaces together. The greater the mass—the amount of matter of an object—the greater the weight and the greater the friction. In this activity, we chose to measure mass because balances are more commonly available than the spring scales used to measure weight.

Sometimes friction is desirable. We want bicycle and car tires to grip the road. Although rubber is a high-friction material, it is the rough surface created by the tire tread that most contributes to friction. Friction is particularly needed under rainy conditions where a layer of water may sit on top of a road lubricated by oils from daily traffic. Car brakes utilize friction to stop the car. We rely upon friction to keep our shoes from slipping on the floor. Friction from striking a match produces a flame. Friction from rubbing a bow against a violin string creates vibrations that make music.

However, friction can be a problem. It produces heat, causes wear and tear on surfaces, and lowers speed.

Friction can be reduced through the use of lubricants. Lubricants smooth out a surface, filling in the nooks and crannies. A dull safety pin coated with soap is easier to use. Oil and grease smooth the surfaces of bearings and gears in machines. Butter may help remove a ring from a swollen finger. Skis are waxed to make them faster on the snow. In the sport of curling, a stone slides across a sheet of ice toward a target as team members sweep the ice with brooms to reduce friction. Desk drawers that stick can be waxed. Silicone, a friction-reducer, is sprayed on squeaky door hinges. Water, talc, and graphite can also be used as lubricants.

Management

1. Choose a flat desk or table at least 50 cm in length. Use books to prop two legs about 10 cm off the floor. Adjust the height if the film canister slides too quickly or doesn't move at all. Tape the piece of cardboard to the edge of the desk to keep the canister from dropping to the floor.

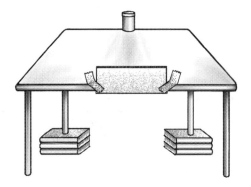

2. If suitable desks or film canisters are in short supply, use large cookie sheets as inclined planes and objects with a mass between 50 and 80 grams, such as olive cans, for sliding.
3. Set up stations, with one desk and film canister designated for each lubricant, including a control left untreated. The inclines need to be the same. Have groups rotate from desk to desk to gather data.
4. Lubricants might include a bar of soap, dishwashing soap mixed with water, wax, vegetable oil, heavy car oil (30- or 40-weight), and so on.
5. Apply the given lubricant to both the desk and the bottom of the film canister. A small piece of sponge is useful for applying oil. Remove excess oil, soap, or other lubricants with a paper towel, leaving a lightly-coated surface; thick coats can actually increase friction.
6. Times will be very fast, sometimes less than a second, requiring close observation and good reflexes. To control variables, line up the back edge of the film canister with the edge of the desk. Start the stopwatch at the moment of release and stop it when the canister hits the cardboard barrier.
7. Increments used for the graph will depend on the range of data. If the longest time is four seconds or less, use increments of .20 (two-tenths of a second).
8. While reading a digital stopwatch is not difficult, interpreting the decimals when constructing a graph can be. Students need to understand where to place 2.84, for example, given the increments on their graphs. It may help to imagine the numbers as hundreds, without the decimals.

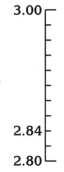

For students ready for more independent work:

Present this *Open-ended Challenge:* You work in a factory. Your product slides down a ramp to get to the next part of the assembly line. Without moving the ramp, how can you increase the sliding speed?

Students should describe the ramp surface, length, and height as well as the product and its mass. Data gathered should be illustrated in some way.

Procedure

Day One: Setting the Stage

1. Ask students to tell about kinds of slides they have used. [playground slides, water park slides, etc.] What makes slides fun? [going fast] What about the slides make them fast? [the smooth metal of a playground slide, the running water going down the water park slide, a mat ridden down a huge plastic slide]
2. Tell students they are going to investigate how to make a slide faster. The more slippery it is, the less friction there is. Explain the slide setup.
3. Have students brainstorm possible lubricants that might reduce friction. From this list, come to a consensus on four or five which are obtainable and would be interesting to test.
4. Encourage students to bring these items the next day.

Day Two: Investigating

1. Instruct each group to set up one slide and apply the lubricant.
2. Distribute the first activity page. Have students record data about the inclined plane and sliding object.
3. Tell students to record three time measurements for each lubricant, including *none,* an untreated surface. Review how to do the timing (see *Management 6*).
4. Have groups rotate until all the lubricants have been tested.
5. Ask students to look at their three slide times for *none* and follow the directions for finding the median average. Have them complete the table.

Surface Treatment	Slide Times	Average Time*
none	3.29	3.53
	4.66	
	3.53	
bar soap	2.18	1.84
	1.63	
	1.84	

6. Give students the graph page and discuss together how to number the increments. Have students label and color the bars according to their data.
7. Direct students to order the lubricants from best (fastest) to worst (slowest) and discuss the results.

Connecting Learning

1. How do the lubricants compare at reducing friction? [Example: on a melamine surface, the oils seemed to reduce friction more than soaps] Were there any that increased friction? If so, why do you think so?
2. How do your results compare with those of other groups? What might explain differences? [amount of lubricant applied to the surface, timing accuracy, etc.]
3. What other variables would affect the results? [surface of ramp, ramp length, ramp height, surface of sliding object, mass of object]
4. Do you think different lubricants would perform better on different surfaces? In other words, is what best reduces friction between metals different than what best reduces friction between plastics or wood?
5. Give examples where you would want to reduce friction in the real world. [all kinds of machinery, slides, skis and sleds on snow, skates on ice, etc.]
6. When would you want to have some friction? [shoes, bicycle or car tires, conveyor belts, to stop roller blades, etc.]
7. What are you wondering now?

* Reprinted with permission from *Principles and Standards for School Mathematics,* 2000 by the National Council of Teachers of Mathematics. All rights reserved.

Slip, Sliding Away

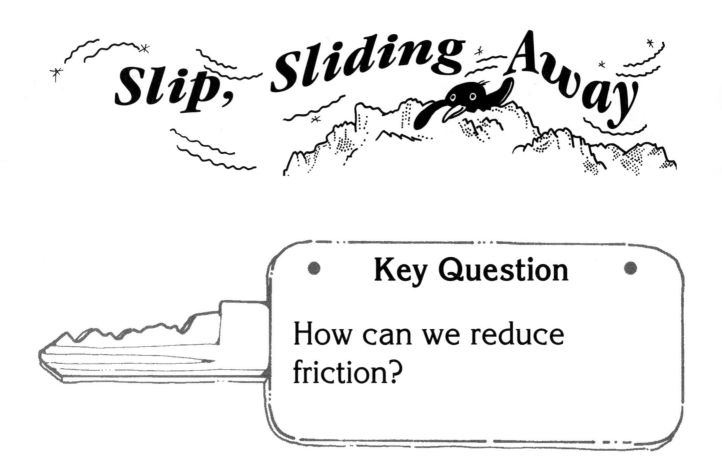

Key Question

How can we reduce friction?

Learning Goal

Students will:

- compare how effective several lubricants are in reducing friction.

Slip, Sliding Away

How can we reduce friction?

Lubricant	Slide Times							Average Time*

*Color the high and low times for each lubricant. Write the remaining number, the median average, in the last column.

Inclined Plane

Surface:

Length:

Height:

Sliding Object

Kind:

Mass:

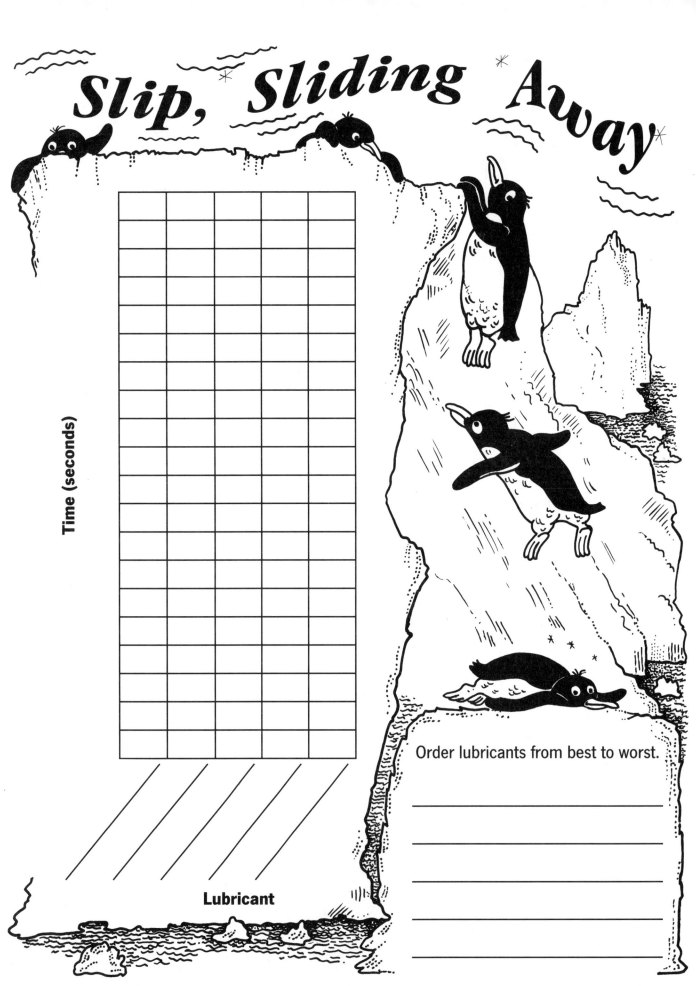

Slip, Sliding Away

Time (seconds)

Lubricant

Order lubricants from best to worst.

_____

_____

_____

_____

Slip, Sliding Away

CONNECTING LEARNING

1. How do the lubricants compare at reducing friction? Were there any that increased friction? If so, why do you think so?

2. How do your results compare with those of other groups? What might explain differences?

3. What other variables would affect the results?

4. Do you think different lubricants would perform better on different surfaces? In other words, is what best reduces friction between metals different than what best reduces friction between plastics or wood?

5. Give examples where you would want to reduce friction in the real world.

6. When would you want to have some friction?

7. What are you wondering now?

Cool Conductors

Topic
Heat conduction

Key Question
How can you use your sense of touch to determine which materials are good heat conductors and which ones are good insulators?

Learning Goals
Students will:
• investigate the conduction of heat energy using their sense of touch, and
• classify materials as (heat) conductors or insulators.

Guiding Documents
Project 2061 Benchmarks
• *When warmer things are put with cooler ones, the warm ones lose heat and the cool ones gain it until they are all at the same temperature. A warmer object can warm a cooler one by contact or at a distance.*
• *Some materials conduct heat much better than others. Poor conductors can reduce heat loss.*

NRC Standard
• *The behavior of individual organisms is influenced by internal cues (such as hunger) and by external cues (such as a change in the environment). Humans and other organisms have senses that help them detect internal and external cues.*

Science
Physical science
   heat energy
      conduction
         conductors and insulators

Integrated Processes
Observing
Comparing and contrasting
Drawing conclusions

Materials
Activity sheet

Background Information
According to the second law of thermodynamics, heat energy flows naturally from hotter objects to cooler ones. When objects are in direct contact, this energy transfer occurs through the process called conduction. Some materials transfer heat energy more easily than others—these materials are called *conductors*. Materials that don't transfer heat energy well are called *insulators*.

When conducting materials are at room temperature, they feel quite cool to the touch since they quickly conduct heat energy away from our warmer bodies (which have a temperature of about 37 degrees Celsius or 98.6 degrees Fahrenheit). Insulating materials at the same room temperature don't feel nearly as cool since they don't conduct heat energy well. Most of us experience this phenomenon in our homes when we walk barefoot from a carpeted area to a tiled area. The carpet is an excellent insulator and prevents body heat from being conducted away. The tile floor, however, is a good conductor and quickly conducts heat away. This makes the tile floor feel cooler than the carpet when in actuality they are both at the same room temperature.

In this activity students will use their senses of touch to determine which materials in their classroom are good conductors and which ones are good insulators—the conductors will feel noticeably cooler to the touch, even though they are really the same temperature as the insulators. To illustrate, the steel leg of a chair feels cool to the touch whereas the wood part of a pencil will not—steel is a good conductor, while wood is a good insulator. Fortunately, air is an excellent insulator; otherwise we would always feel cold at room temperature.

Management
1. This activity is meant to be done in the classroom. It works best when heating or cooling units are not in use. These units create different temperature zones within the classroom that are problematic.
2. Students will need to know the difference between objects and the materials making up the objects. For example, a pencil (object) is composed of many different materials (wood, rubber, graphite, etc.). If this distinction is not clear, discuss it beforehand.

3. Caution students not to include materials in their investigation that are not at room temperature—the plastic on the top of a running computer monitor, for example.

4. Ask students not to touch things they are testing for more than a few seconds. When conductors are in contact with warmer objects like students' hands, those objects quickly absorb enough heat energy to raise their temperatures above room temperature.

Procedure

1. Distribute the student sheet.
2. Ask the *Key Question:* "How can you use your sense of touch to determine which materials are good heat conductors and which ones are good insulators?"
3. Have students follow the directions on the student sheet. After they complete the activity, lead them in a class discussion.

Connecting Learning

1. What did you notice when you touched your pencil and then the steel leg of your chair? [The steel felt cooler than the wood.]
2. What other materials did you touch?
3. Which ones felt cool?
4. Which ones didn't?
5. Are these different materials really different temperatures? [no]
6. What temperature are they? [room temperature]
7. Why do some things feel cooler than others? [The materials that feel cooler are better conductors.]
8. What happens when you walk barefoot from a carpeted room to one with tile? [The tile feels cooler.]
9. In terms of what you've learned in this activity, explain what happens. [The carpet feels warmer than the tile since it doesn't conduct the heat away from your foot. In actuality, the carpet and tile are both at the same room temperature.]
10. What are you wondering now?

Extensions

1. Have students investigate to see if different areas of skin feel the apparent temperature differences created by conduction better than others. Some areas to try are the side of the face, the neck, the back of the hand, and the arm.
2. Have students experience heat energy flowing into them instead of away from them by touching materials that are warmer than room temperature, (but not hot enough to burn!). Some things to try are their foreheads (which are often warmer than hands), the top of a running computer monitor, the sidewalk outside on a sunny day, or a metal tetherball pole in the sun.

Cool Conductors

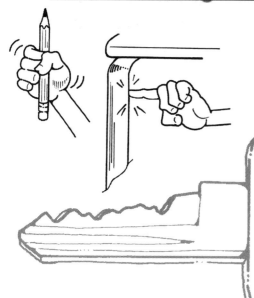

Key Question

How can you use your sense of touch to determine which materials are good heat conductors and which ones are good insulators?

Learning Goals

Students will:

- investigate the conduction of heat energy using their sense of touch, and

- classify materials as (heat) conductors or insulators.

Cool Conductors

Using your sense of touch, how can you determine which materials are good heat conductors and which ones are good insulators?

Touch the wooden part of your pencil and then touch the steel leg of your chair.
What do you notice? Which feels cooler to the touch, wood or steel?

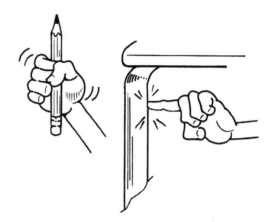

Touch various other materials in the room. Which ones feel cool to the touch? Which ones don't? Make a list of these materials below.

Cool to the touch:	**Not cool to the touch:**

What similarities, if any, do you see in the above lists?

Cool Conductors

What's happening:

Scientists have learned that heat flows naturally from warmer things to cooler ones. Although the different materials in the room feel like they are at different temperatures, they are not. They are all about the same temperature, which we call room temperature.

What makes some materials feel cooler than others is their ability to conduct heat away from your (warmer) body when you touch them. These materials are called conductors since they conduct or transfer heat well. The materials that don't conduct heat as well are called insulators. These materials don't feel as cool to the touch.

Now, think about what happens when you walk barefoot from a room with carpet to a room with tile. In terms of what you've learned in this activity, explain what happens.

Cool Conductors

CONNECTING LEARNING

1. What did you notice when you touched your pencil and then the steel leg of your chair?

2. What other materials did you touch?

3. Which ones felt cool?

4. Which ones didn't?

5. Are these different materials really different temperatures?

6. What temperature are they?

7. Why do some things feel cooler than others?

8. What happens when you walk barefoot from a carpeted room to one with tile?

9. In terms of what you've learned in this activity, explain what happens.

10. What are you wondering now?

95   © 2004 AIMS Education Foundation

H🍫T CH🍫C🍫LATE

Topic
Heat transfer: conduction

Key Question
By what pattern will the chocolate chips melt?

Learning Goal
Students will gather evidence about the direction in which heat is conducted by observing the melting patterns of chocolate chips.

Guiding Documents
Project 2061 Benchmarks
- *Some materials conduct heat much better than others. Poor conductors can reduce heat loss.*
- *Heating and cooling cause changes in the properties of materials. Many kinds of changes occur faster under hotter conditions.*

NRC Standard
- *Heat can be produced in many ways, such as burning, rubbing, or mixing one substance with another. Heat can move from one object to another by conduction.*

NCTM Standard 2000*
- *Select and apply appropriate standard units and tools to measure length, area, volume, weight, time, temperature, and the size of angles*

Math
Measurement
    time
    length
Whole number operations
    subtraction (elapsed time)
Graphing
    timeline

Science
Physical science
    heat energy
        conduction
        changes in matter

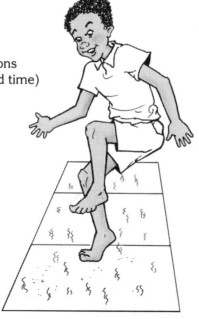

Integrated Processes
Observing
Collecting and recording data
Comparing and contrasting
Interpreting data
Predicting
Relating

Materials
For each group:
    11 chocolate chips
    votive candle, about 5 cm tall
    matches
    heavy-duty aluminum foil (see *Management 3*)
    metal spoon (see *Management 4*)
    toothpicks, one for each student
    2 tin cans, 14-16 oz., labels removed
    timer with second hand or digital stopwatch

For the class:
    fire extinguisher
    adult supervision for each group

Background Information
Conduction is the flow of heat through a material from areas of higher temperature to areas of lower temperature. This can be from one area of a material to another or from one material to another material in direct contact. If you hold a metal spoon, the heat energy from your warmer hand is conducted to the cooler spoon. Your hand actually warms it up.

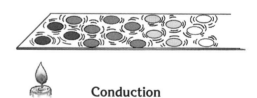

Conduction

In this activity, a candle flame radiates heat energy to the molecules in the foil directly above it. These molecules start to vibrate rapidly, bumping into nearby molecules and passing energy to them. This next set of vibrating molecules, in turn, bumps into their neighbors and passes the heat energy on. The molecules do not travel along the solid; they just vibrate in place, bumping against their neighbors in a game of "Pass It On." Through this process of conduction, heat energy is carried along the foil bridge.

The conduction of heat energy slows down as it travels further from the heat source. At some point, the heat stops being conducted because the heat is lost to radiation faster than it is being conducted.

There are three observations students should make as a result of doing this activity: 1) Heat energy moves from warmer areas to cooler areas. 2) Heat energy travels outward from the area closest to the heat source. 3) Heat transfer slows down as it gets further from the source of heat.

Management

1. While it is recognized that open flames are not allowed in all schools, heat energy cannot be explored without a heat source. Take every precaution necessary to ensure a safe environment. Have an adult (parent volunteer, aide, etc.) with each group during the entire investigation. Keep a fire extinguisher handy.

2. Stress safety issues with students.
   - Remove coats and tie long hair back.
   - Place a cafeteria tray or other non-flammable material under the work space.
   - Have adults light and extinguish the candle.
   - Suggest students move carefully as sudden movements can jar the setup.
   - Do not eat the chocolate since it will have been touched.

3. Each group will need one piece of aluminum foil (24 cm x 30 cm) for the bridge, a smaller piece to make a foil cylinder for the candle, and another piece (at least 15 cm square) to place under the candle for safety reasons.

4. For increased safety, hold a regular spoon with a clothespin or use a longer-handled iced tea spoon.

5. The tin cans support the foil and chips without a problem but you may choose to add marbles, sand, or water to the cans to further anchor them.

6. It is preferable for all groups to work on the activity at the same time. A single class demonstration is not recommended because students will not be able to make detailed observations from a distance.

Procedure

Part One

1. Ask, "What do you notice about the chips in chocolate chip cookies just out of the oven?" [They look soft and shiny.] "How did they get that way?" [from the oven heat] Explain that today the class will observe the direction heat travels by watching the melting patterns of chocolate chips.

2. Review safety rules (see *Management 2)* and distribute the first activity page. Instruct groups to collect materials and go to their observation sites.

3. Ask the adults to light the candle on the tray and hold the spoon with one chip above the flame. Have students talk about what they observe.

4. Extinguish the candle. Encourage students to take turns poking the chip with their toothpicks and allow time for them to write how the chip changed.

5. Have each group prepare the foil bridge according to the directions, making it as smooth as possible so the chips will be in full contact. To help direct its heat energy upward, ask the adults to make a foil cylinder (rising within 2 cm of the bridge) to slip around the candle.

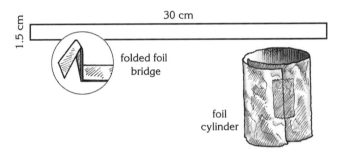

6. Define for students when a chip starts melting: when the bottom edge begins to turn glossy or shiny. To feel the change from cold to warm, sensing firsthand that heat energy travels through solids, have students touch the bridge at the *opposite end* from the candle before it is lit and, later, after it is extinguished.

7. Slip the foil cylinder over the candle, light it, and move it under the far left chip. Record the starting time, if calculating elapsed time, or start the stopwatch.

8. Have students record the time each chip starts to melt, then number the order in which they melt. (The last chip may not receive enough heat energy to begin melting.) Extinguish the candle.

9. Distribute the second page and instruct students to cut and glue the chips on the timeline according to their results. The timeline is divided into 10-second increments.

Part Two

1. Repeat the investigation with the candle in the center. Have students predict the melting pattern (using the same number for any chips they think will melt at the same time) and the total melting time.

2. Ask the adults to replace the five melted chips (now cooled) with five new ones, light the candle, and move it under the center chip.

3. Have students write the starting time and the time the last chip starts to melt on the edge of the paper, calculate the elapsed time, and number the chips to show the actual melting pattern.

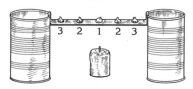

4. Discuss the experience. Give students time to think and write about their observations as they complete the activity page.

Connecting Learning

1. Describe the chocolate chip when it came out of the bag. [hard or solid, smooth, brown with a bit of white coating, etc.] Describe the chocolate chip after it was placed over the candle. [soft, shiny, changing from solid to liquid, gooey, etc.]

2. How do your results compare with those of other groups? What might cause differences? [how carefully measuring directions were followed (distance between candle and bridge, distance between chips), person's judgement about when melting started]

3. In what kind of pattern did the heat energy travel? [outward from the flame, the heat source]

4. Did the chips melt at even time intervals? [no] How would you describe the melting time pattern? [The further the chip was from the flame, the longer it took for sufficient heat to be conducted to melt it.]

5. How does your total melting time for the first and second investigations compare? [When the candle was in the center, the chips melted faster.] How might this be explained? [All the chips were closer to the center candle and heat energy was traveling in two directions at the same time.]

6. If you put the candle under the second chip, what melting pattern would you expect?

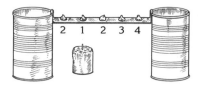

7. Using *cool* and *hot,* describe the flame and foil at the beginning of the activity. [The flame was hot; the foil was cool.] Which one, flame or foil, changed the temperature of the other one? [The flame heated the foil.] If heat energy travels from warm to cool, in what direction would it move in the pictures on the second page? [from tongue to ice cream, from hand to spoon, from sidewalk to foot]

8. What conducted the heat in this activity?

9. What are you wondering now?

HOT CHOCOLATE

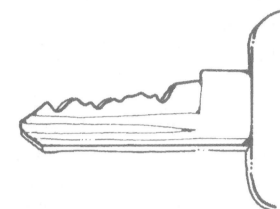

Key Question

By what pattern will the chocolate chips melt?

Learning Goal

Students will:

- gather evidence about the direction in which heat is conducted by observing the melting patterns of chocolate chips.

H⬥T CH⬥C⬥LATE

By what pattern will the chocolate chips melt?

Caution: An adult should be with your group at all times. Ask the adult to light the candle for you.

Chip	Time started melting
1	:
2	:
3	:
4	:
5	:

Observe one chip as it melts. Tell the chip's story.

Fold the foil in half four times. Bend each end and hook over the cans.

Adjust the height so it is 4 cm above the top of the candle. Place five chips 3 cm apart. Put the candle at the far left. Number the chips in the order they melt.

Glue paper chips (next page) on the timeline to show when each started to melt.

Melting Time in Minutes

0 1 2 3 4 5 6 7

H✦T CH✦C✦LATE

Number the chips to show the melting pattern.

Predicted Melting Pattern

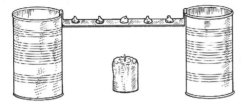

Actual Melting Pattern

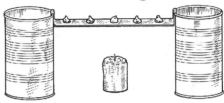

Predicted total melting time: _____

Actual total melting time: _____

(Total melting time is the time needed for the last chip to start melting.)

How did closeness to the flame affect the chips?

Look at what things were warm and what things were cool.
Did the heat energy travel from warm to cool or cool to warm?

Draw arrows to show the direction
the heat energy would move
in these pictures.

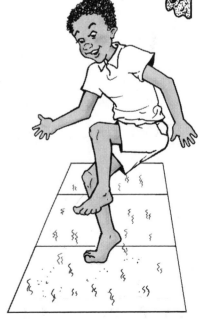

Color the chips brown. Cut and glue them on the timeline.

✂

HOT CHOCOLATE

1. Describe the chocolate chip when it came out of the bag. What did the chocolate chip look like after it was placed over the candle?

2. How do your results compare with those of other groups? What might cause differences?

3. In what kind of pattern did the heat energy travel?

4. Did the chips melt at even time intervals? How would you describe the melting time pattern?

5. How does your total melting time for the first and second investigations compare? How might this be explained?

6. If you put the candle under the second chip, what melting pattern would you expect?

7. Using *cool* and *hot,* describe the flame and foil at the beginning of the activity. Which one, flame or foil, changed the temperature of the other one? If heat energy travels from warm to cool, in what direction would it move in the pictures on the second page?

8. What conducted the heat in this activity?

9. What are you wondering now?

Topic
Insulation of ice

Key Question
How long can you keep an ice cube from melting?

Learning Goal
Students will design ways to insulate an ice cube.

Guiding Documents
Project 2061 Benchmarks
- *Heating and cooling cause changes in the properties of materials. Many kinds of changes occur faster under hotter conditions.*
- *Some materials conduct heat much better than others. Poor conductors can reduce heat loss.*

NRC Standards
- *Heat can be produced in many ways, such as burning, rubbing, or mixing one substance with another. Heat can move from one object to another by conduction.*
- *Heat moves in predictable ways, flowing from warmer objects to cooler ones, until both reach the same temperature.*
- *Materials can exist in different states—solid, liquid, and gas. Some common materials, such as water, can be changed from one state to another by heating or cooling.*

NCTM Standards 2000*
- *Develop fluency in adding, subtracting, multiplying, and dividing whole numbers*
- *Select and apply appropriate standard units and tools to measure length, area, volume, weight, time, temperature, and the size of angles*
- *Represent data using tables and graphs such as line plots, bar graphs, and line graphs*

Math
Measurement
   mass
   time
Whole number operations
   subtraction
Bar graph

Science
Physical science
   heat energy
      insulators

Integrated Processes
Observing
Collecting and recording data
Comparing and contrasting
Interpreting data

Materials
For each group:
   1 ice cube in a small plastic bag (see *Management 3*)
   balance
   gram masses

Background Information
Water forms ice at 0°Celsius (32° Fahrenheit). When exposed to temperatures above freezing, ice remains at 0°C, but begins to melt as it absorbs the heat energy from its surroundings. Heat energy travels from the warmer air to the cooler ice. Conductors speed up this movement but insulators slow it down. The challenge of this activity is to find a good way to insulate the ice cube.

Insulating materials might include cotton batting, newspaper, various kinds of fabric, foam peanuts, dirt, etc. Students should conclude that materials vary in their effectiveness; some materials are better insulators than others. Construction techniques can also play a role. Because air is an insulator, air pockets trapped within crumpled newspaper, for example, provide more insulation than flat layers of the same material.

Management
1. This activity has three sections: constructing the *Polar Brrr*, gathering the experimental data, and examining the class results. Allow two or more periods for the initial planning and construction of the *Polar Brrr*, followed by the experiment and analysis of results on another day(s). Students should work in groups of two or three.
2. Permit students who forget their materials to use available classroom supplies.

3. The day before, make ice cubes with the same size and shape. Just before distributing, put each ice cube in a plastic bag.
4. Allow one to two hours to elapse between the beginning and ending measurements.
5. Placement of the *Polar Brrrs* is an important variable to control. The conditions should be uniform for the class, that is, no sun exposure or unusual drafts.

Procedure

1. Ask students how long they think it takes an ice cube to melt, given the current air temperature. Gather their oral responses and write them down. Then ask what they might do to keep an ice cube from melting. Take a few suggestions before introducing them to the made-up term, *Polar Brrr*, which refers to the "structure" they will build to keep an ice cube from melting. Explain the rules:
   • Any materials may be brought in except an electrical appliance, a thermos, or an ice chest.
   • The *Polar Brrr* must fit on top of a desk.
   • To avoid messes, the ice cube will remain in a plastic bag during the experiment.
2. Group students and have each group devise a plan. Give them a day or two to bring in materials and assemble their *Polar Brrrs*.
3. Give each student the first activity page. Direct them to make a drawing of their *Polar Brrr* and list the materials they used to build it.
4. On the experiment day, have each group set up a balance, obtain gram masses, and place their *Polar Brrr* on their desk or in a designated area. Explain that when each group gets an ice cube, students should carefully find the mass and immediately place the ice into the *Polar Brrr*. The time and beginning mass should be noted on the activity page.

   Optional: At the same time, leave an ice cube in a plastic bag out in the room as a control. Have students compare the melting of this non-insulated cube to those with *Polar Brrr* protection.
5. Give each group one ice cube in a plastic bag and have them proceed with the experiment.
6. After the given waiting period, (see *Management 4*), instruct students to record the ending time, then drain the melted water from the plastic bags and find the ending mass.
7. Direct students to determine the elapsed time and write a number sentence to show how the mass changed.
8. For class comparisons, arrange the *Polar Brrrs* in order along a counter and label each with its corresponding letter. Give students the graph page and oversee the gathering of data from each group.
9. Have students complete the bar graph, study it and the *Polar Brrrs*, and determine which types of insulation worked best.

Connecting Learning

1. How did your ice cube change?
2. What caused it to melt? [the warmer air around it] What would happen if the temperature were below freezing? [It would remain ice.]
3. What kind of insulating material worked best? (The class might order the materials from most to least successful.)
4. What other kinds of materials might you try if the activity were repeated?
5. If you were taking refrigerated or frozen food to a picnic, how would you insulate it? Is your idea practical? (consider expense, bulkiness, etc.)
6. What are you wondering now?

Extensions

1. Put ice cubes in different places to test melt rates (in the sun, in the shade, in the refrigerator, in a closet, etc.).
2. Have students find the ending mass of the ice cube *with* the melted water and compare that to the beginning mass. It should be the same.
3. Discuss how ice was obtained and kept before refrigeration. [Lake ice was cut in large blocks during the winter and kept in insulated houses covered with sawdust until used.]
4. Investigate the insulating properties of snow by doing the activity, "Cold Comfort" (*AIMS®*, Vol. XII, No. 6).
5. Journal Prompt: Compose a poem, make a cartoon strip, or write a story about the life of an ice cube.

* Reprinted with permission from *Principles and Standards for School Mathematics,* 2000 by the National Council of Teachers of Mathematics. All rights reserved.

Key Question

How long can you keep an ice cube from melting?

Learning Goal

Students will:

- design ways to insulate an ice cube.

Team: _____

How long can you keep an ice cube from melting?

Construction

Build a Polar Brrr, something that will keep your ice cube from melting, using everyday materials. It must fit on top of your desk.

Polar Brrr

Materials

Beginning

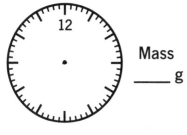

Mass

_____ g

_____ : _____

Your Results

Draw the clock hands and record the time.
Find the mass of the ice cube.

How much time elapsed?

Write a number sentence showing how the mass changed.

Ending

Mass

_____ g

_____ : _____

POPPING WITH POWER   106   © 2004 AIMS Education Foundation

Ending Mass of Ice Cubes

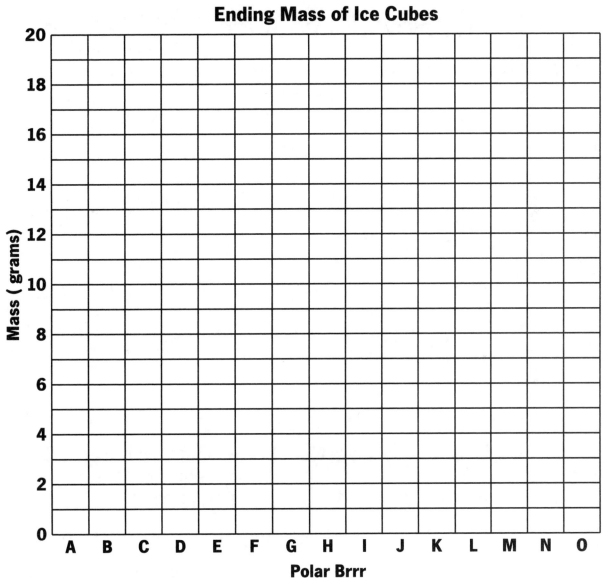

Mass (grams)

20
18
16
14
12
10
8
6
4
2
0

A   B   C   D   E   F   G   H   I   J   K   L   M   N   O

Polar Brrr

Which Polar Brrr(s) worked best?

What made it successful?

1. How did your ice cube change?

2. What caused it to melt?
   If the temperature were below freezing, what would happen?

3. What kind of insulating material worked best?

4. Order the materials from poorest insulating materials to best insulating materials.

5. What other kinds of materials might you try if the activity were repeated?

6. If you were taking refrigerated or frozen food to a picnic, how would you insulate it? Is your idea practical? Explain.

7. What are you wondering now?

CARTONS 'N' COTTON

Topic
Heat insulation

Key Question
How can we slow down the loss of heat?

Learning Goal
Students will compare the effects of cotton-insulation with non-insulation on jars of hot tap water.

Guiding Documents
Project 2061 Benchmarks
- People try to conserve energy in order to slow down the depletion of energy resources and/or to save money.
- Some materials conduct heat much better than others. Poor conductors can reduce heat loss.

NRC Standards
- Heat can be produced in many ways, such as burning, rubbing, or mixing one substance with another. Heat can move from one object to another by conduction.
- Heat moves in predictable ways, flowing from warmer objects to cooler ones, until both reach the same temperature.

NCTM Standards 2000*
- Select and apply appropriate standard units and tools to measure length, area, volume, weight, time, temperature, and the size of angles
- Collect data using observations, surveys, and experiments

Math
Whole number operations
    subtraction
Measurement
    temperature
    time
Line graph

Science
Physical science
    heat energy
        insulation
Environmental science
    conservation of energy

Integrated Processes
Observing
Collecting and recording data
Comparing and contrasting
Controlling variables
Interpreting data
Relating

Materials
For each group:
    3 uniform, small jars with lids such as large baby
        food jars
    3 half-gallon milk cartons
    scissors
    glue
    cotton balls, approximately 64 large or 110+ regular
    3 thermometers
    hot tap water
    masking tape

Background Information
One way heat moves is by conduction. The heat energy is passed on by direct contact, moving from warmer areas to cooler areas. The heat energy in this activity moves from the hot water to the cooler glass to the cooler air close to the glass.

Materials that are poor conductors, such as cotton, are good insulators; they reduce the rate of heat loss. Insulators are most effective when in direct contact with the heated matter, in this case the jar holding the hot water.

Hot chocolate, tea, and coffee are more enjoyable if they stay hot. We use foam or other kinds of insulated cups to slow the loss of heat.

However, there is another reason to be concerned about heat loss—conservation. To reduce energy use and help us save money, today's water heaters have a glass lining (a good insulator), coupled with a foam insulation blanket between the lining and the outer shell. Older water heaters without the foam insulation can be wrapped with insulation blankets. Insulation slows the cooling of the water so the heating element does not have to be used as often. Insulation wrapped around water pipes exposed to freezing weather helps keep the water from turning to ice and cracking the pipes.

Insulation applies to solids as well. Insulation in the walls of buildings reduces the use of furnaces and air conditioners. So does the layer of air between the sheets of double-paned windows. Insulated clothing, such as down jackets and vests, keep our body heat from escaping during cold weather.

Management

1. Have students prepare the milk cartons on one day and conduct the investigation the next day.
2. Divide the class into groups of four to six, depending on available materials.
3. It is less confusing if thermometers in a given group start with matching temperature readings, though the differences between beginning and ending temperatures will be the final means of comparison.
4. Plan for the 15-minute wait periods, perhaps with a read-aloud book.

Procedure

Day One

1. "On a cold day, how do you keep warm?" (putting on a jacket, covering up with a blanket, etc.) "How can we slow down the loss of heat in a hot liquid?" After fielding suggestions, explain that they will be investigating ways to keep hot water warm as long as possible using cotton balls.
2. Give each group three cartons, the cotton balls, and glue. Direct them to mark the cartons at the 10-cm height and, on one side, at the 20-cm height. Have them cut along the highest mark on each side, then fold the 20-cm side in half to form a lid.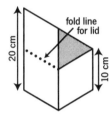
3. Instruct each group to glue cotton balls to the outside of one carton on all six sides, on the inside of another carton on all six sides, and leave the third untouched. To minimize mess, have students make a line of glue across the carton and press the cotton balls against it.

Day Two

1. Have each group gather their prepared cartons, three jars, and three thermometers. Tell them to label the jars *outside, inside,* and *none* with masking tape.
2. Fill each jar with about the same amount of hot tap water. Immediately have students insert a thermometer in each jar, wait for the thermometer to register the water temperature, and record.
3. Direct students to remove the thermometers, place lids on the jars, put each jar in a carton, and close the lid with a piece of masking tape or weight with a crayon box. To ensure that the same thermometer is used with the same carton, have students lay each thermometer by its respective carton.
4. Wait 15 minutes. Have students quickly open the cartons, remove the jar lids, insert the thermometers, and record the temperatures.
5. After students have removed the thermometers and replaced the lids, wait another 15 minutes.
6. Tell groups to measure and record the temperatures as before.
7. Have students complete the key and line graph.
8. Discuss the results.

Connecting Learning

1. How did we control variables? [same kind and size of jars, same material and size of cartons, same starting water temperature]
2. What variable did we test? [two methods of insulation versus none]
3. What happened to the temperature of the water in each jar?
4. Which jar lost the most heat? [no insulation]
5. Which jar retained the most heat? [cotton inside] What are some possible reasons why that happened? [The cotton was directly touching the jar, like a blanket, protecting the heat from escaping into the surrounding air. Cotton is a poor heat conductor.]
6. How might you explain the results for the carton with cotton outside? [The insulation did not directly touch the jar so it had less of an effect in slowing the loss of heat.]
7. Describe or draw a picture of how the heat moves in this activity. [It moves from warmer to cooler by direct contact—from the hot water to the cooler jar to the air next to the jar.]
8. What are the sources of hot water in our homes? [water heater, pipes] Why is it important to insulate these sources? [to conserve energy, to save money, to keep pipes from cracking in freezing weather]
9. What are you wondering now?

Extensions

1. Investigate how animals are insulated. How do they prepare for winter?
2. How do we insulate our bodies? How about people who live in Alaska?

Curriculum Correlation

Literacy

Have individual students or groups write the sequence of steps they followed in this activity. Instruct them to write each step on a strip of paper, order the strips, and attach them to another paper with tape. The strips can also be combined into paragraphs.

Conservation

Have students design a poster showing ways to insulate to save energy.

Home Link

Encourage students to investigate what kind of insulation their water heater has and/or what their parents do to protect pipes in the winter.

* Reprinted with permission from *Principles and Standards for School Mathematics,* 2000 by the National Council of Teachers of Mathematics. All rights reserved.

CARTONS 'N' COTTON

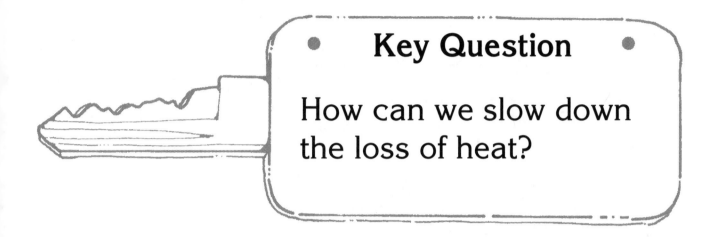

Key Question

How can we slow down the loss of heat?

Learning Goal

Students will:

- compare the effects of cotton-insulation with non-insulation on jars of hot tap water.

CARTONS 'n' COTTON

How can we slow down the loss of heat?

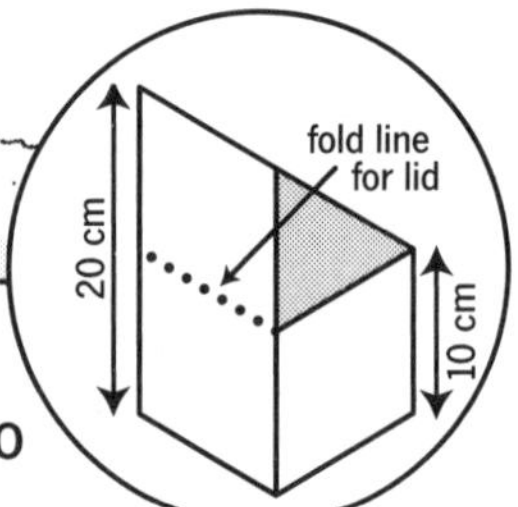

Directions
- Cut three half-gallon milk cartons to make 10 cm x 10 cm cubes.
- Glue cotton balls to the outside of one carton, the inside of another carton, and leave the third carton alone.
- Measure temperature changes in small jars of hot tap water kept in these cartons.

20 cm

fold line for lid

10 cm

Time	Temperature		
	cotton outside	none	cotton inside
Difference (beginning-ending)			

What is your conclusion?

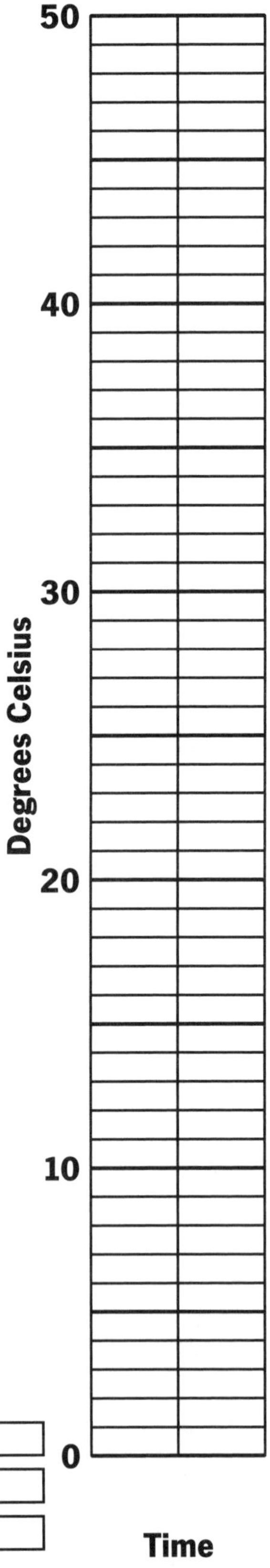

Degrees Celsius

50

40

30

20

10

0

Time

Key

outside ☐

none ☐

inside ☐

CARTONS 'n' COTTON

1. How did we control variables?

2. What variable did we test?

3. What happened to the temperature of the water in each jar?

4. Which jar lost the most heat?

5. Which jar retained the most heat? What are some possible reasons why that happened?

6. How might you explain the results for the carton with cotton outside?

7. Describe or draw a picture of how the heat moves in this activity.

8. What are the sources of hot water in our homes? Why is it important to insulate these sources?

9. What are you wondering now?

PUFF MOBILES

Topic
Creative engineering/wind energy

Key Questions
1. How can you use the force of the wind to move your *Puff Mobile?*
2. How can you improve your design for greater distance?

Learning Goals
Students will:
- design and construct straw sail cars powered by their own wind energy, and
- modify their designs to increase travel distance.

Guiding Documents
Project 2061 Benchmarks
- *Something that is moving may move steadily or change its direction. The greater the force is, the greater the change in motion will be. The more massive an object is, the less effect a given force will have*
- *Moving air and water can be used to run machines.*
- *There is no perfect design. Designs that are best in one respect (safety or ease of use, for example) may be inferior in other ways (cost or appearance). Usually some features must be sacrificed to get others. How such trade-offs are received depends upon which features are emphasized and which are down-played.*

NRC Standards
- *The position and motion of objects can be changed by pushing or pulling. The size of the change is related to the strength of the push or pull.*
- *An object's motion can be described by tracing and measuring its position over time.*
- *Design a solution or product.*
- *Evaluate a product or design.*

NCTM Standards 2000*
- *Select and apply appropriate standard units and tools to measure length, area, volume, weight, time, temperature, and the size of angles*
- *Represent data using tables and graphs such as line plots, bar graphs, and line graphs*

Math
Estimation
Measurement
   length
Graphs

Science
Physical science
   force and motion
   kinetic energy

Technology
Structure and design

Integrated Processes
Observing
Controlling variables
Collecting and recording data
Comparing and contrasting
Hypothesizing

Materials
For each group:
   10 plastic drinking straws
   4 wheels (see *Management 1*)
   straight pins
   1 sheet of 8 1/2" x 11" paper
   meter sticks or tapes (see *Management 2*)

For the class:
   stopwatch or timer with second hand

Background Information
This activity is an exercise in creative engineering that uses the wheel as a simple machine and a sheet of paper to "catch the energy" of the wind. The force or push of the wind puts the *Puff Mobile* in motion, demonstrating that wind can be used to perform work. *Work* is done whenever a *force* is used to move something over a *distance*. Friction is a force that opposes motion. If the friction is great enough, it can cancel the push and the object does not move at all.

The design and modification process, however, is the heart of this activity. Students begin with a challenge requiring divergent thinking: create a design which will move as far as possible in a linear direction. As they test and modify their *Puff Mobiles*, they will make informal hypotheses about what design changes will work. Through testing and retesting, they will start to converge on a design that will best achieve this goal.

Management
1. For wheels you plan to reuse, purchase wooden beads with holes that will accommodate straws easily. If students are going to keep their *Puff*

Mobiles, use mint-flavored hard candy with a center hole as wheels.

2. Copy the meter tape at the back of this book on several bright colors of paper. Assemble, laminate, and give two to each student. By linking the variously-colored tapes together, students can easily see how many meters their *Puff Mobiles* traveled.

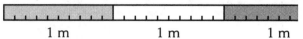

1 m　　　　1 m　　　　1 m

3. The day before, tell students to wear clothing that is suitable for working and racing on their knees.
4. Groups of two or three are suggested. Jobs might include Puffer, Recorder, and Timer.
5. Allow extended time to do the whole activity on one day. If you are going to organize the races as a tournament, construct and modify the designs one day and conduct the tournament on a second day.
6. The graphs should be done after the three trials have been completed and the range can be determined. Though the graphs are separated, they must be numbered in the same way so comparisons can be made among them.

Procedure

Part One

1. Challenge small groups to build a vehicle that, by blowing, will move the farthest in five seconds. Explain that each group must use 10 straws, 4 wheels, straight pins, and 1 sheet of paper, no more and no less. The paper and straws can be cut, but all the pieces must be used.
2. Distribute the construction materials and the two activity pages.
3. Have students construct, name, and sketch their original designs on the pages.
4. Guide the class in determining the racing rules: starting position, from what part of the car to measure, number of puffers allowed, etc.
5. On the first page, have each group record the estimated distance their *Puff Mobile* will travel during the first trial, using meters (such as 6.2 m) or centimeters (such as 620 cm).
6. Conduct and time the first trial. Instruct students to measure and record the distance traveled next to the estimate.

Part Two

1. Ask, "How can you improve your design for greater distance?"
2. Have students record at least one problem they want to correct, briefly describe the change they will make, modify the *Puff Mobile,* and sketch the new design.
3. Direct students to estimate, test, measure distances, and make design changes again.
4. Have students estimate, test, and measure distances one more time.

5. Ask students to complete the graphs of their three trials. To help students determine how to number the graphs, have them identify the range between the shortest and longest distances. All graphs should be numbered alike so comparisons can be made between trials.
6. Pair sets of *Puff Mobiles* and conduct the races.

Connecting Learning

1. Why is wind considered a contact force? [A force is a push or pull. The moving air directly touches and pushes against things.] What did the wind contact in this activity? [sail]
2. What other parts of the *Puff Mobile* help it move? [The round wheels roll, producing less friction than if the mobile rested on flat objects such as cubes.]
3. How far did your first *Puff Mobile* travel in five seconds?
4. How did you modify your *Puff Mobile?*
5. Did it travel farther than before? Explain.
6. To improve the travel distance, what else might you try? [possibly a different blowing technique]
7. What objects in our world use the wind to move? [sailboats, windmills, etc.]
8. What are you wondering now?

Extensions

1. Pool the successful ideas from all of the groups and build an even better *Puff Mobile*. Challenge another class to a race.
2. Have each group report their best distance and make a class bar graph of the data, individually or on one large chart.
3. Try a 30-second race. A number of puffers will be necessary for each *Puff Mobile*.
4. Roll the *Puff Mobiles* down an inclined plane. Record, graph, and compare results.
5. Assessment idea: Design a *Puff Mobile* that will move on water. Agree on the materials to be used.
6. For one day or more, have students make a list of objects they see with wheels—in the real world, on screen, or in print. Examples might include wheels in the kitchen (pizza cutter), wheels in the garage (cars, bicycles), wheels for recreation (roller blades), historic wheels (water wheel, grinding wheel), among others.
7. Collect and display pictures of wind being used as an energy source.

Resource

Caney, Steven. *Steven Caney's Invention Book.* Workman Publishing. New York. 1985. (Includes 35 stories of how people experimented and refined their designs, from earmuffs to roller skates.)

* Reprinted with permission from *Principles and Standards for School Mathematics,* 2000 by the National Council of Teachers of Mathematics. All rights reserved.

PUFF MOBILES

Key Questions

1. How can you use the force of the wind to move your *Puff Mobile?*

2. How can you improve your design for greater distance?

Learning Goals

Students will:

- design and construct straw sail cars powered by their own wind energy, and
- modify their designs to increase travel distance.

PUFF MOBILES

How far can you blow your Puff Mobile in five seconds?

Build a Puff Mobile using 10 straws, four "wheels," straight pins, and one sheet of paper. You may cut the straws and paper, but you must use all of the materials.

_____
Name of Puff Mobile

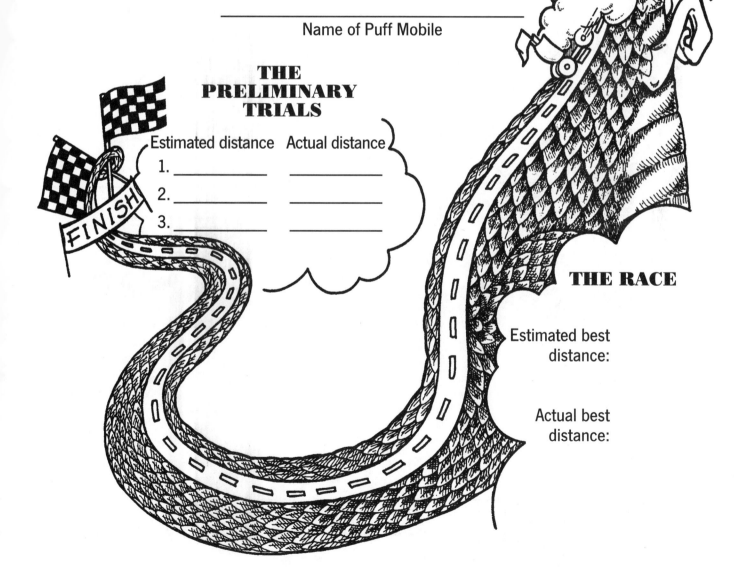

THE PRELIMINARY TRIALS

Estimated distance   Actual distance

1. _____ _____

2. _____ _____

3. _____ _____

THE RACE

Estimated best
distance:

Actual best
distance:

Modified MOBILES

Original Design

Design, test, and modify your Puff Mobile three times. Graph the distance traveled in each trial.

TRIAL #1

Problems   **Changes**   **Design #2**

TRIAL #2

Problems   **Changes**   **Design #3**

TRIAL #3

PUFF MOBILES

1. Why is wind considered a contact force? What did the wind contact in this activity?

2. What other parts of the *Puff Mobile* help it move?

3. How far did your first *Puff Mobile* travel in five seconds?

4. How did you modify your *Puff Mobile?*

5. Did it travel farther than before? Explain.

6. To improve the travel distance, what else might you try?

7. What objects in our world use the wind to move?

8. What are you wondering now?

Wind Rollers

Topic
Wind energy/wind patterns

Key Question
What does the roller show you about the wind?

Learning Goals
Students will use rollers to:
- explore the kinetic energy of the wind, and
- make observations about wind patterns.

Guiding Documents
Project 2061 Benchmarks
- *Air is a substance that surrounds us, takes up space, and whose movement we feel as wind.*
- *Something that is moving may move steadily or change its direction. The greater the force is, the greater the change in motion will be. The more massive an object is, the less effect a given force will have.*

NRC Standards
- *An object's motion can be described by tracing and measuring its position over time.*
- *The position and motion of objects can be changed by pushing or pulling. The size of the change is related to the strength of the push or pull.*

NCTM Standards 2000*
- *Describe, name, and interpret direction and distance in navigating space and apply ideas about direction and distance*
- *Describe location and movement using common language and geometric vocabulary*
- *Select and apply appropriate standard units and tools to measure length, area, volume, weight, time, temperature, and the size of angles*

Math
Estimation
Measurement
    length
Geometry and spatial sense
    direction

Science
Physical science
    kinetic energy
    force and motion
Earth science
    meteorology

Integrated Processes
Observing
Collecting and recording data
Comparing and contrasting

Materials
Tagboard or 6" paper plates
Scissors
Metric tapes or sticks
Optional: metric trundle wheel

Background Information
Wind has kinetic energy, the energy of moving things. *Kinetic* comes from a Greek word for *move*. Wind can push or lift things. The tagboard roller has potential energy, energy stored or at rest. When the wind pushes against the triangular sails or blades on the roller, it moves. The roller's potential energy has been changed into kinetic energy.

Several observations can be made about microclimate wind patterns from watching the wind roller in action. There is a pattern of wind currents around buildings and on the playground. The path of the currents may be straight, curved, up and down, or a combination of these. The force or speed of wind varies, sometimes dying down and then starting up again within a few seconds. A real-time graphic of wind speed and direction, sometimes shown during televised golf games, demonstrates how variable or steady the wind can be.

Management
1. Duplicate the *Construction* page on tagboard or, if using paper plates, on copy paper.
2. Wind rollers can be made individually, but should be tested with a partner who can help with measuring.
3. This activity should done on a windy day; light breezes are not strong enough to make the rollers move.
4. The starting position for the wind roller does not matter. It can be set on the ground or thrown in the air.
5. Let students set the rules for releasing the wind rollers and measuring the distance traveled.

Procedure

1. Tell students they will each be making a wind roller that will help them learn about the energy of the wind. Briefly discuss *potential* and *kinetic* energy.
2. Give students either the tagboard *Construction* page or the paper plates and copy paper *Construction* page. Have them follow the directions to make their wind rollers.
3. Distribute the second activity page and have students estimate the distance their wind rollers will travel.
4. Group pairs of students. Instruct each pair to take their wind rollers, a measuring tool, recording page, and pencil outside.
5. Have students release their wind rollers three times, measuring and recording the distance traveled after each trial.
6. Tell student pairs to circle each person's longest wind roller distance.
7. Encourage students to discuss their observations and then answer the questions on the activity page.

Connecting Learning

1. How did the wind make the roller move? [It pushes against the blades.]
2. What kind of energy does the wind have? [kinetic energy] How would you describe this kind of energy? [It is the energy of moving things.]
3. Before the roller began to move, what kind of energy did it have? [potential energy]
4. What wind patterns did you notice? [It blew at different speeds, it moved in different directions, it went north the whole time, etc.]

5. What else can the wind do besides causing our wind rollers to move? [dries clothes, blows trash, moves dirt and sand, breaks down rock, pumps water, generates electricity, etc.]
6. Compare your best distance with others in the class. What things (variables) might affect the distance traveled? [For similar wind rollers, two variables are the amount of wind at that moment and friction from the type of surface over which it rolls. For different wind rollers, size, material used, and the number of blades might be factors.]
7. How could we improve our wind rollers? (See *Extension 1.)*
8. What are you wondering now?

Extensions

1. Form teams to make a better wind roller. Experiment with size, material, and number of blades.
2. Build and test other wind catchers such as gliders.

Curriculum Correlation

Literacy

1. Write a story about some adventures you had while chasing your wind roller around your neighborhood, town, or state.
2. Read selections from *Windy Day: Stories and Poems* edited by Caroline Feller Bauer (J.B. Lippincott, New York, 1988).

* Reprinted with permission from *Principles and Standards for School Mathematics,* 2000 by the National Council of Teachers of Mathematics. All rights reserved.

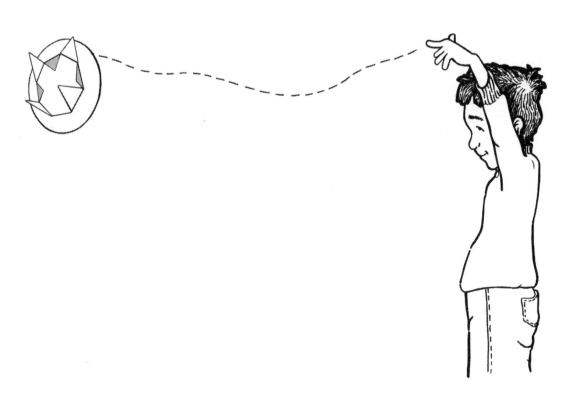

Wind Rollers

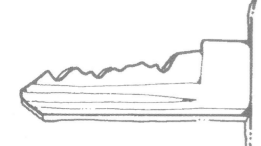

Key Question

What does the roller show you about the wind?

Learning Goals

Students will:

- use wind rollers to explore the kinetic energy of the wind, and
- make observations about wind patterns.

Wind Rollers
Construction

Copy this pattern on tagboard or use with 6-inch paper plates.

1. Cut out the circle.
2. Punch a small hole in the center and cut along the dotted lines.
3. Fold the points back along the hexagon, alternating up and down folds.

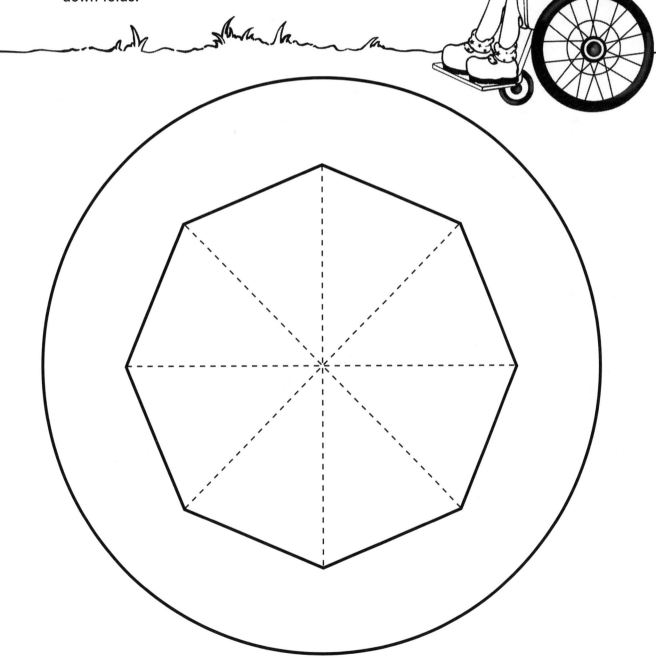

Wind Rollers

What does the roller show you about the wind?

Estimate how far your wind roller will travel:

Measure and record three trials each for you and another person. Circle each person's best trial. How do your distances compare?

Name	Distance		
	Trial 1	Trial 2	Trial 3

What did you observe about the path of the wind?

What did you observe about the force of the wind?

Wind Rollers

1. How did the wind make the roller move?

2. What kind of energy does the wind have? How would you describe this kind of energy?

3. Before the roller began to move, what kind of energy did it have?

4. What wind patterns did you notice?

5. What else can the wind do besides causing our wind rollers to move?

6. Compare your best distance with others in the class. What things (variables) might affect the distance traveled?

7. How could we improve our wind rollers?

8. What are you wondering now?

Topic
Wind energy

Key Question
How can we capture the wind's energy to make things spin?

Learning Goal
Students will design and construct objects that spin in the wind.

Guiding Documents
Project 2061 Benchmarks
- *Moving air and water can be used to run machines.*
- *Even a good design may fail. Sometimes steps can be taken ahead of time to reduce the likelihood of failure, but it cannot be entirely eliminated.*
- *Make sketches to aid in explaining procedures or ideas.*

NRC Standards
- *The position and motion of objects can be changed by pushing or pulling. The size of the change is related to the strength of the push or pull.*
- *Evaluate a product or design.*

NCTM Standard 2000*
- *Recognize and apply mathematics in contexts outside of mathematics*

Math
Spatial sense
Measurement (dependent on designs)

Science
Physical science
    wind energy
    force and motion

Technology
Structure and design

Integrated Processes
Observing
Comparing and contrasting
Relating

Materials
For each group:
    plastic straw
    9-oz paper or Styrofoam cup
    10-cm circle
    masking tape
    pushpin
    10-inch to 12-inch bamboo skewer
    large shoebox or similar-sized box
    scissors
    ruler

For the class:
    two or more hole punches
    more plastic straws
    paper and card stock

Background Information
A force is a push or a pull. Wind is a force that pushes. It pushes against a surface such as the sail on a boat. It flows around an airfoil, like an airplane's wing or a wind turbine's rotor blades, creating another force—lift. It pushes against the sails of a windmill. How far or fast objects move is directly related to the strength of the wind.

Wind moves; therefore, it has kinetic energy—the energy of motion. This energy can be harnessed to do work, including the generation of electricity. It all starts with an object that can spin. A spinner, attached to a shaft, can be connected to gears, pulleys, generators, or other machines. A spinner attached to a pulley, for example, can be used to lift a crayon from the floor to a chair. Kinetic energy is transferred from the wind to the spinner to the machine.

Since the 600s in Persia (now Iran), windmills have been used to grind grain, water crops, saw lumber, produce electricity, etc. A modified model of a vertical English windmill introduces this activity. The original windmill pumped water; ones large enough to generate electricity for utility companies were thought to be too costly. This model was chosen because it is such a different construction from the typical Dutch windmill most people picture or the pinwheel many children have seen or made. Hopefully, it will spark creativity as students design different kinds of spinning objects.

Management

1. Make copies of the spinner base, one per group, on card stock.
2. Collect building materials in a place accessible to students.
3. Groups of two or three are recommended.
4. *Part Two* may be done in class or as an independent project at home.
5. Depending on the designs created, measuring tools such as rulers and drawing compasses may be helpful.

Procedure

Part One

1. Show the class the windmill picture. Ask what part of the windmill catches the wind. [the sails, sometimes called arms or wings] With your finger, trace how the motion of the spinning sails is transferred to gears, then to a shaft attached to a grinding stone. Tell students that this is one way grain was ground hundreds of years ago.

   Explain that if we can get an object to spin, it can be attached to a machine to do work. Tell students that they will begin exploring spinning objects by building a different kind of wind spinner.
2. Give students the first activity page and read the first paragraph together.
3. Instruct groups to gather their building materials and construct the spinner, following the directions on the page.
4. To determine versatility, urge students to test the spinner with the wind coming from a variety of directions.

Part Two

1. Tell students they will now have a chance to create their own wind spinners. Distribute *Part Two* and have the class read the information.
2. Suggest each person or small group build their design around a straw shaft and use the spinner holder to test it. Have materials available, though some students may wish to bring additional materials from home.
3. Allow time for students to design, construct, test, and modify their spinners.
4. Have students describe their projects—the series of steps they took and their final outcome—on the activity page. If assessing this page, state your standards.

5. Reflect together about the design process and about how wind spinners relate to doing work in the real world.

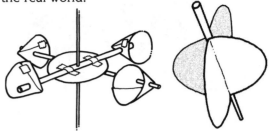

Examples of wind spinners

Connecting Learning

Part One

1. How is this spinner different from the windmill in the picture? [Two examples: It has two curved surfaces while the other windmill has four fairly flat sails. The spinning parts are mounted on a vertical shaft while the sails on the other windmill are attached to a horizontal shaft.]
2. What wind direction(s) made it spin?

Part Two

1. Which were your best spinners? (Have students define *best*.)
2. What about these spinners do you think makes them winners? [enough surface area to push against, open spaces for the wind to enter, spaced surface areas for the wind to keep the spin going, etc.]
3. What wind direction(s) made each one spin?
4. How could a wind spinner be made to do work? [by connecting it to a pulley, gears, a generator, etc.]
5. What are you wondering now?

Extension

Challenge students to construct a wind spinner/pulley system to raise a crayon or another light object from the floor.

Resource

Woelfle, Gretchen. *The Wind at Work: An Activity Guide to Windmills.* Chicago Review Press. Chicago. 1997.
This student-friendly guide to the history of windmills, from early Persian models to modern wind turbines, includes many pictures and plenty of pleasing projects related to science, energy conservation, art, and cooking. It also lists some existing windmills that can be visited in the United States, Canada, England, and the Netherlands.

*   Reprinted with permission from *Principles and Standards for School Mathematics,* 2000 by the National Council of Teachers of Mathematics. All rights reserved.

WIND SPINNERS

Key Question

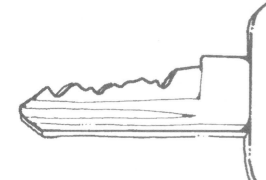

How can we capture the wind's energy to make things spin?

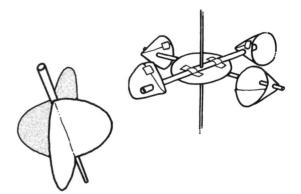

Learning Goal

Students will:

- design and construct objects that spin in the wind.

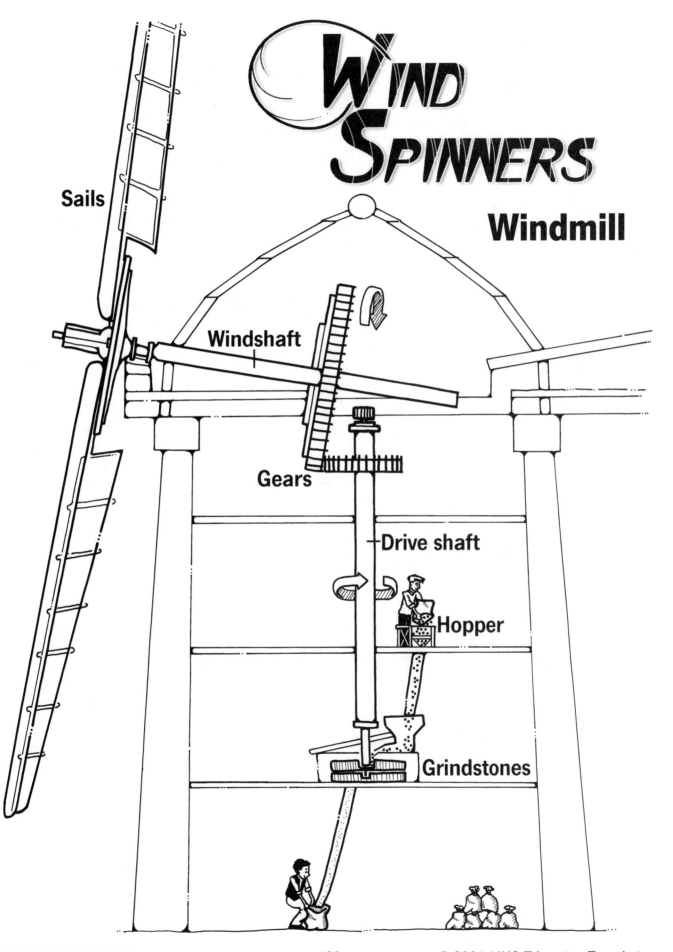

Windmill

Sails

Windshaft

Gears

Drive shaft

Hopper

Grindstones

Wind Spinners

Spinner Bases

WIND SPINNERS

How can we capture the wind's energy to make things spin?

If you can get something to spin, it can be attached to gears, pulleys, or other machines to do work. That is the idea behind windmills. Since the 600s, windmills have been used to grind grain, pump water, make paper, and do several other jobs. Wind turbines, a special kind of windmill, have generators that produce electricity.

Start thinking about spinning designs by building this modified version of a windmill that was used in England to pump water.

Materials

Plastic straw
10-inch bamboo skewer
9-oz paper cup
10-cm circle
Masking tape
Hole punch
Pushpin
Scissors
Large shoebox
Metric ruler

Spinner

A

1. Use a straight edge and pencil to mark cutting lines on the cup. Cut the cup in half. (A)
2. Cut out a spinner base. Have an adult punch out the center hole.
3. Tape one half-cup along the diameter, as shown. (B)
4. Tape the other half-cup on the opposite side, as shown.

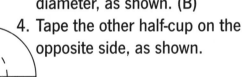

B
half-cup rim
half-cup rim

5. Join the two half-cups at the top with tape, leaving a space just wide enough for the straw. (C)
6. Punch a hole in the center of the tape.

C

D

7. Push the straw through the holes in the base and top. Tape the straw to the spinner. (D)

Spinner Holder

1. Mark the center of the long side of the box, 1 to 2 cm below the top edge. Do the same on the opposite side. Use a pushpin to start a hole at each mark.
2. Thread the skewer through the spinner straw. Work the skewer through the shoebox holes. Hold the box so the straw is in a vertical position.
3. Test the spinner by blowing or by using a hair dryer or fan. Try different directions.

131

WIND SPINNERS Part Two

Challenge: Design and construct an object that will spin when blown.

If you can get something to spin, it can be attached to gears, pulleys, or other machines to do work. You may have made a pinwheel before. What other kinds of designs might spin?

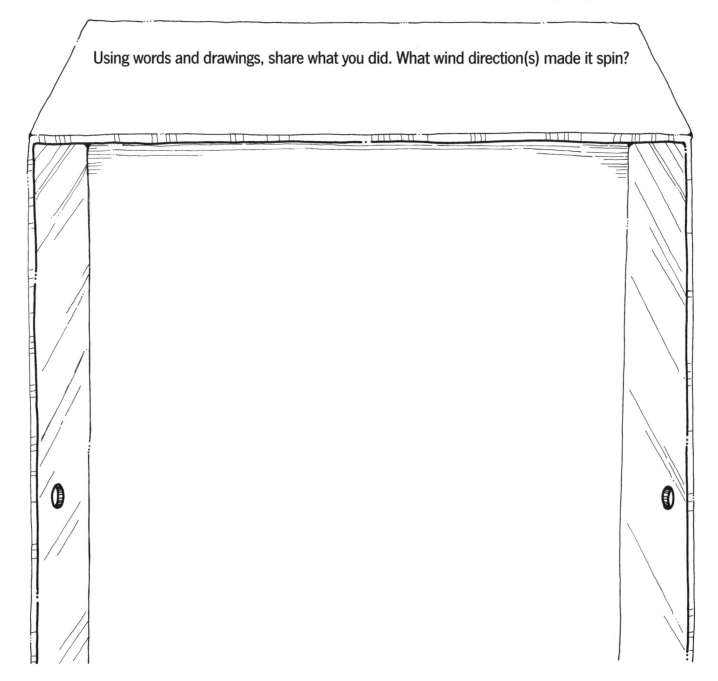

Using words and drawings, share what you did. What wind direction(s) made it spin?

WIND SPINNERS

Part One

1. How is this spinner different from the windmill in the picture?

2. What wind direction(s) made it spin?

Part Two

1. Which were your best spinners?

2. What makes them "best"?

3. What wind direction(s) made each one spin?

4. How could a wind spinner be made to do work?

5. What are you wondering now?

Windmills

Topic
Wind energy and conservation

Key Questions
1. How can the wind be used to do work?
2. How can the wind contribute to our energy resources?

Focus
Students will use the provided text as the foundation for a variety of interdisciplinary activities involving science, math, history, geography, poetry, research, and technology.

Guiding Documents
Project 2061 Benchmarks
- *Moving air and water can be used to run machines.*
- *Some energy sources cost less than others and some cause less pollution than others.*
- *Any invention is likely to lead to other inventions. Once an invention exists, people are likely to think up ways of using it that were never imagined at first.*
- *Technologies often have drawbacks as well as benefits. A technology that helps some people or organisms may hurt others—either deliberately (as weapons can) or inadvertently (as pesticides can). When harm occurs or seems likely, choices have to be made or new solutions found.*

NRC Standards
- *Some objects occur in nature; others have been designed and made by people to solve human problems and enhance the quality of life.*
- *Resources are things that we get from the living and nonliving environment to meet the needs and wants of a population.*
- *The supply of many resources is limited. If used, resources can be extended through recycling and decreased use.*
- *Technological solutions have intended benefits and unintended consequences. Some consequences can be predicted, others cannot.*
- *Science and technology have advanced through contributions of many different people, in different cultures, at different times in history. Science and technology have contributed enormously to economic growth and productivity among societies and groups within societies.*

Science
Physical science
   wind energy
   compound machines
Environmental science
   conservation
      renewable resources

Technology
Structure and design

Literacy
Reading in a content area

Materials
Picture of a Dutch windmill

Management
The student text about windmills leads to related activities in several curricular areas. While students will have a richer experience by doing all of the activities, time restrictions may lead you to choose one or two.

Procedure
1. Show a picture of a Dutch windmill. Ask, "For what do you think this windmill was used?" Tell the class that they will be learning about windmills long ago and the wind turbines of today.
2. Give students *Predict and Check* and have them write true or false in response to each statement.
3. Distribute the text and have students read *The Science of Wind Energy* and *A Short History of Windmills*. Do the timeline activity.
4. Read *Types of Turbines* and do the related writing activity.
5. Read *More about Turbines*. To get an idea of the size of these machines, try one or both of the measurement activities.
6. Read *Wind Farms*. Choose from among the three suggested geography activities.
7. Read and discuss *Wind Energy Pros and Cons*.
8. Have students complete *Predict and Check*. Answers: 1-T, 2-T, 3-F, 4-T, 5-F, 6-T

Connecting Learning
1. What kinds of jobs have wind machines performed?
2. How has the technology of wind machines changed over time?
3. Why are renewable resources important?
4. How are the *Cons* of wind energy being improved and made more acceptable?
5. What do you think about using wind turbines to produce electricity?

Resources
Woelfle, Gretchen. *The Wind at Work: An Activity Guide to Windmills*. Chicago Review Press. Chicago. 1997. (This student-friendly guide to the history of windmills includes many pictures and plenty of pleasing projects related to science, energy conservation, art, and cooking. It also lists some existing windmills that can be visited.)

http://www.windpower.org/
(Accessible in five languages, this Danish website covers a range of wind energy topics, from how a turbine works to environmental concerns. The "Wind with Miller" section has interactive experiences intended for students in grade 5 on up.)

Windmills

Predict and Check

Before you read, write T (true) or F (false) in the left column.

Before Reading   **After** Reading

_____ 1. Windmills have been used for more than 1000 years. _____

_____ 2. Wind turbines change the wind's energy into electricity. _____

_____ 3. To spin, turbines must face into the wind. _____

_____ 4. Wind turbines operate within a certain wind speed range. _____

_____ 5. Wind turbines can be useful in any location. _____

_____ 6. Wind energy is a renewable resource. _____

After you read, write T (true) or F (false) in the right column. Rewrite false statements so they are true.

Windmills

How can the wind be used to do work?

The Science of Wind Energy

Wind is moving air. Something that is moving has motion energy—kinetic energy. Windmills change the wind's energy into power (mechanical energy). The power is used to grind grain, pump water, produce electricity, and do many other jobs.

A Short History of Windmills

People have been using the wind's energy for hundreds of years. As early as the 600s, windmills were used to grind grain and water crops in Persia (now Iran). About the 1200s, windmills spread across Europe—the Netherlands, Denmark, England, France, Germany and Eastern Europe. Windmills produced power for sawing lumber, grinding grain, pressing oil from seeds, grinding pigment for paint, and making paper, among other jobs. Around the 1600s, the Dutch began to use windmills to pump water from low lands. This made more land available for farms and towns.

By the mid 1800s, Australian and American farmers were using the wind to pump water for crops and cattle. Over time, windmills also provided power to saw wood, lift grain into silos, pump water from mine shafts, and crush ore.

In 1892, Poul LaCour, a native of Denmark, found a way to make a windmill generate electricity. In the 1920s and 1930s, small windmills provided power for lights and appliances on many farms in the United States. By the 1940s, electric and gasoline engines replaced windmills. Most windmill companies went out of business by the 1950s.

In the 1970s, there was an increasing demand for electricity. Oil shortages made the problem worse. These events created new interest in using wind power. The wind turbine, a streamlined windmill that produces electricity, was developed. The word **turbine** comes from the Latin **turbo**, which means spinning object.

Poul la Cour

Windmill Timeline

- Make a timeline showing the history of windmills. When, where, and how was wind energy used?

Windmills

Types of Wind Turbines

There are two basic kinds of wind turbines. The most common turbine has a **horizontal axis** mounted on a tall tower or pole. It has two or three blades that look like large airplane propellers. Turbines with three blades usually work facing into the wind. Turbines with two blades generally face away from the wind.

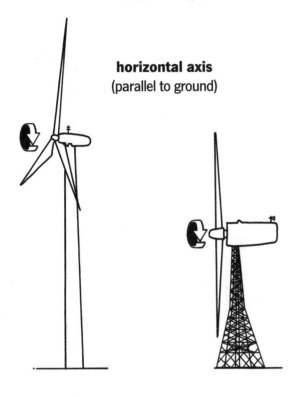

horizontal axis
(parallel to ground)

In the 1920s, a Frenchman named George Darrieus invented a wind turbine with a **vertical axis**. It looks like a giant eggbeater, with two or three curved blades attached to a vertical shaft. This turbine can capture the wind from any direction. It is one of several kinds of vertical turbines now used.

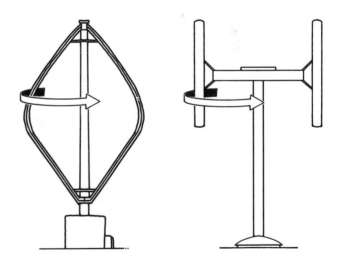

vertical axis
(perpendicular to ground)

Wind Turbine Poetry

- After looking at wind turbine pictures, write a simile, a four-line poem, or a cinquain describing one of the types.

Windmills

More about Turbines

Wind turbines all have the same basic parts. A set of blades called the rotor is mounted on a tower often more than 30 meters (100 feet) tall. The wind causes the rotor to spin. This spins the shaft that connects to a generator and makes electricity. Cables carry the electric current down the tower and underground to power lines that distribute the energy to nearby towns.

Turbines operate when the wind speed is between 7 and 55 miles per hour. If the wind is at least 7 mph, the rotors will turn fast enough to produce electricity. The angle of the blades can be changed to catch more or less of the wind. This keeps the rotor moving at a constant speed even though the wind speed may change. To prevent damage from winds above 55 mph, there is a system for slowing and then stopping the rotors.

A single, small wind turbine can provide electrical power for a farm, small business, or even a school. It will probably have a tower between 80 and 120 feet tall and produce less than 50 kilowatts of power.

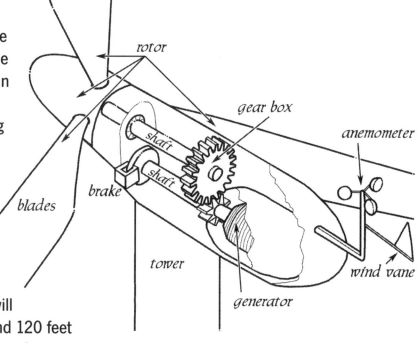

Groups of larger wind turbines, called wind farms, can generate electricity that feeds into the utility lines of a city or county. Twenty years ago, an average utility turbine had a power rating of 150 kilowatts. The turbines now being installed are usually rated at 700 kilowatts or more. Larger blades and taller towers help increase the amount of energy produced. Because wind speed increases with height, taller towers can capture more of the wind's energy.

Measuring a Turbine

• How does a small wind turbine compare to you?
  Outdoors, make a life-sized outline of a small wind turbine.

• How do small and large wind turbines compare?
  Make a scale drawing comparing two turbines of different sizes.

Wind Farms

Turbines are built in windy areas—across open plains, on smooth hills, near shorelines, and between mountain gaps. For small turbines, average wind speeds need to be greater than 9 mph. Large wind power plants need speeds of at least 13 mph.

Europe is the present leader in the use of wind power. Denmark produces 15 percent of its energy using wind power. The United States produces less than 1 percent. California, however, has the three largest wind farms in the world. Altamont Pass, the Tehachapi Mountains, and San Gorgonio Pass together have more than 15,000 wind turbines.

According to the American Wind Energy Association (www/awea.org), the following ten countries generated over 95% of the wind energy produced in 2001.

Country	Capacity in Megawatts*
Germany	8750
United States	4261 **
Spain	3337
Denmark	2417
India	1407
Italy	697
Netherlands	483
United Kingdom	474
China	399
Sweden	290

 * 1 million watts

** In the United States, the average household uses about 10,000 kWh of electricity each year. The electricity produced from present wind power sources can supply over one million homes.

Wind Farm Geography

• On a world map, find and color the top ten countries using wind energy. A map page follows.

• Are there wind farms in your state? If so, where are some of them located?

• Find a wind power map on the Internet. In what areas of the United States is it windy enough to consider developing wind farms? Where would wind farms not be a reasonable choice?

© 2004 AIMS Education Foundation

Windmills

How can the wind contribute to our energy resources?

Pros

- Wind energy is a renewable resource. It will always be there.

- Wind energy is clean. It does not pollute the air, water, or land.

- The use of wind energy reduces the need for oil from foreign countries.

Cons

- Wind varies in speed and direction. Sometimes it does not blow at all. Some areas are not windy enough to use wind power.

- Not everyone likes the way wind farms look. Sometimes the windiest spots are the most beautiful and people want to preserve that beauty. It is more pleasing to the eye if wind farms have the same type and size of turbines and they are evenly spaced.

- Electrical energy generated by the wind is more costly than from other sources, about 5 cents per kilowatt-hour in the mid 1990s. To lower costs, larger turbines that produce more electricity are being developed.

- Noise used to be a problem with some early wind turbines. Now a turbine 250 meters from a house produces no more noise than a kitchen refrigerator.

- Danger to birds is a concern at a few specific sites such as Altamont Pass, but bird deaths from wind energy are far fewer than those from airplanes, cars, buildings, hunters, and cats.

Today, more powerful wind turbines are being developed. The cost of electricity from wind power is getting lower. There is interest in renewable energy sources. The U.S. Department of Energy has set a goal that, by 2020, 5% of our electricity will come from wind power.

Windmill Timeline

Key Question
When, where, and how has wind energy been used?

Learning Goals
Students will:
- use the provided information to make a timeline showing the history of windmills, and
- relate the timeline to their own lives.

Guiding Documents
Project 2061 Benchmark
- *Geometric figures, number sequences, graphs, diagrams, sketches, number lines, maps, and stories can be used to represent objects, events, and processes in the real world, although such representations can never be exact in every detail.*

NRC Standards
- *People have always had problems and invented tools and techniques (way of doing something) to solve problems. Trying to determine the effects of solutions helps people avoid some new problems.*
- *Science and technology have been practiced by people for a long time.*

NCTM Standards 2000*
- *Represent data using tables and graphs such as line plots, bar graphs, and line graphs*
- *Use representations to model and interpret physical, social, and mathematical phenomena*

Math
Graphing
Ordering events

Literacy
Gathering data from a reading passage
Sequencing

Integrated Processes
Interpreting data

Materials
Scissors
Tape or glue

Procedure
1. After students read *A Short History of Windmills*, distribute the timeline page.
2. Tell students to cut out the three strips and join them into one strip with tape or glue.
3. Have students number the timeline, using the starting numbers to determine the pattern. [counting by hundreds]
4. Ask students how many years the shorter lines represent. [ten years]
5. Instruct students to add the names of places and/ or persons at the appropriate dates, along with a phrase describing each event.
6. Have students study and answer questions using the timeline.

Connecting Learning
1. Have you ever seen a windmill or wind turbine? If so, describe what it looked like and where you saw it.
2. How long ago were windmills first used? [600 subtracted from the present year]
3. According to the timeline, which of these events have happened in your lifetime? …in your parent's lifetime? …in your grandparent's lifetime? (Students should understand that the interest in wind turbines, starting in the 1970s, is continuing today.)
4. What other observations can you make by studying the timeline?
5. How is a timeline useful? [It shows how events are distributed over time, sometimes close together and sometimes far apart.]

Home Link
Students might ask their parents or grandparents about experiences they may have had with windmills or wind turbines.

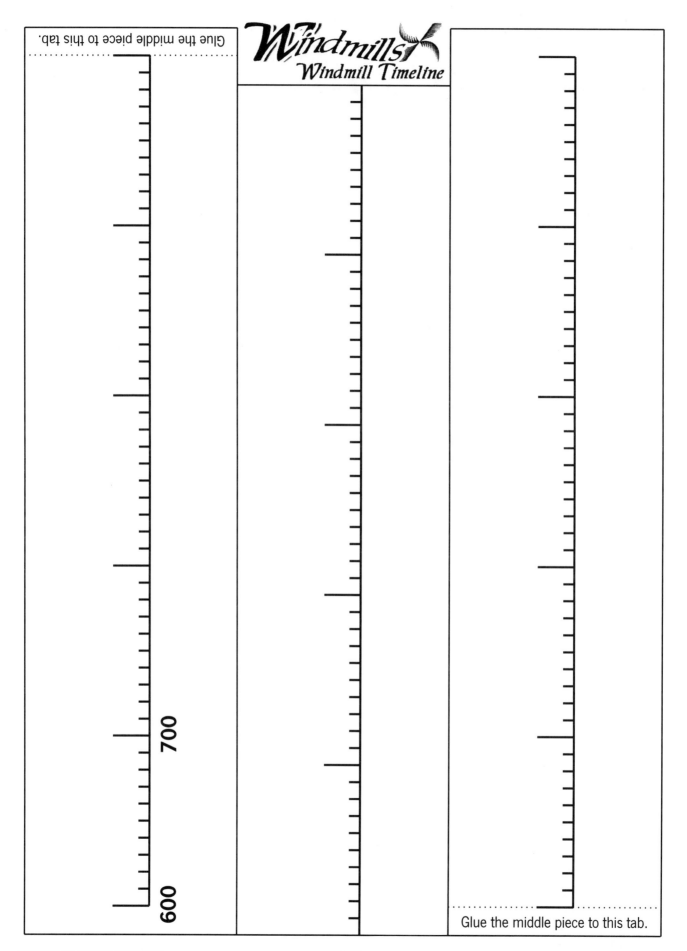

Windmills — Wind Turbine Poetry

Key Question
How can wind turbines be described?

Learning Goal
Students will use similes or poetry to describe one type of wind turbine.

Guiding Documents
Project 2061 Benchmark
* *Any invention is likely to lead to other inventions. Once an invention exists, people are likely to think up ways of using it that were never imagined at first.*

NRC Standard
* *People continue inventing new ways of doing things, solving problems, and getting work done. New ideas and inventions often affect other people; sometimes the effects are good and sometimes they are bad. It is helpful to try to determine in advance how ideas and inventions will affect other people.*

Literacy
Poetic or comparative descriptions

Materials
Pictures of wind turbines

Procedure
1. After students read *Types of Wind Turbines,* show them pictures from books, the Internet, etc.
2. Brainstorm words related to wind turbines, recording them in a place visible to the class.
3. Introduce the style of writing you wish to have students practice: similes, four-line poetry with or without a rhyming pattern, or cinquains. If cinquains are chosen, give students the activity page.
4. Have students create their descriptions using the style you have prescribed.
5. Encourage students to share their work in small groups. Some may wish to share with the whole class.

Connecting Learning (small group)
1. What did you like about each person's writing?
2. What type of wind turbine was he or she describing? What words were used that helped you to know?

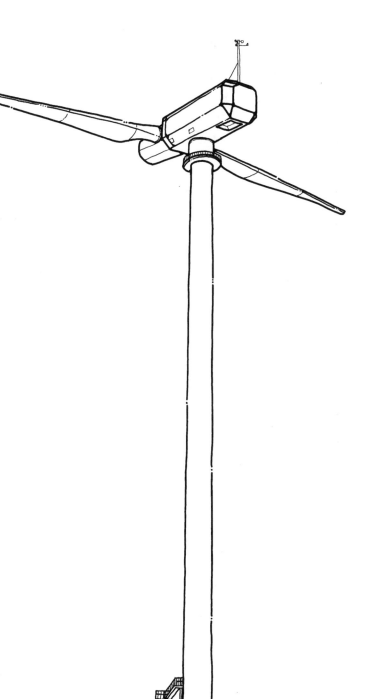

Windmills — Cinquains

Cinquain is a five-line poem describing a subject according to a certain pattern.

Line	Number and kind of words	Example
1st	one subject (naming) word	snowflakes
2nd	two adjectives (describing)	white, silent
3rd	three verbs (action)	falling, drifting, melting
4th	four or five words expressing a feeling	soft kiss on your nose
5th	another word for subject	ice crystals

Brainstorm words related to your chosen topic.

Try some cinquains.

_____

_____

_____

_____

_____

_____

_____

_____

_____

_____

Windmills — Measuring a Turbine

Key Questions
1. How does the height of a small wind turbine compare to you?
2. How do small and large wind turbines compare?

Learning Goals
Students will get an idea of the size of wind turbines by:
- making a life-sized outline of a small wind turbine outdoors, and/or
- making a scale drawing comparing two turbines of different sizes.

Guiding Documents
Project 2061 Benchmarks
- *Geometric figures, number sequences, graphs, diagrams, sketches, number lines, maps, and stories can be used to represent objects, events, and processes in the real world, although such representations can never be exact in every detail.*
- *Scale drawings show shapes and compare locations of things very different in size.*

NRC Standard
- *Objects have many observable properties, including, size, weight, shape, color, temperature, and the ability to react with other substances. Those properties can be measured using tools, such as rulers, balances, and thermometers.*

NCTM Standards 2000*
- *Select and apply appropriate standard units and tools to measure length, area, volume, weight, time, temperature, and the size of angles*
- *Recognize and apply mathematics in contexts outside of mathematics*

Math
Measurement
    length
    angle (optional)
Scale drawing

Integrated Processes
Observing
Comparing and contrasting

Materials
Transparency of the first activity page
Metric trundle wheel or long metric tape
Thick yarn
Craft sticks or golf tees
Chalk (for asphalt)
Drawing compass, optional
Protractor, optional

Management
1. All students should do the life-size outline of a wind turbine outdoors. Do the scale drawing if it is appropriate for your class.
2. To draw the rotor blades and visualize their sweep, it is helpful to set a drawing compass with the radius measurement (diameter ÷ 2). Draw a circle with the top of the tower at the center. Draw a straight line from the center to the edge of the circle. This will become the first blade. Equally space the second and third blades using a protractor.
3. If drawing 120° angles for a three-blade rotor is difficult, provide a template like the one shown below or have students eyeball it. Another option is for students to draw a two-blade rotor.

Procedure
1. After reading *More about Turbines*, put a transparency of the first activity page on the overhead projector. Ask, "How does the height of a small wind turbine compare to you?" Read the information together.
2. Have students gather the materials and take them to a playground area large enough to outline the small wind turbine.
3. Using the lengths given on the page, instruct students to measure and outline a tower with yarn held in place by craft sticks or golf tees. For asphalt, use chalk.
4. For the rotor, have students make the diameter line and draw two blades. The center of the line should pass through the top of the tower.
    More capable students can compute the radius and draw three blades, either using a protractor to space them 120° apart or using an eyeball estimate.
5. To compare the turbine to students, tell them to stand at the base of the tower.
6. Back inside, give students the scale drawing page and have them follow the directions.

Connecting Learning
1. What part was the most difficult to outline or draw? [probably the rotor blades] How did you do it?
2. How would you describe the size of wind turbines?
3. How does the height of wind turbines help them do their job? [Wind speed increases with height, so taller towers can capture more energy.]
4. What are you wondering now?

Windmills — Measuring a Turbine

How does a small wind turbine compare to you?

Wind turbines come in many different sizes and power ratings. Some produce less than 50 kW* of electricity at a time. Others produce more than 1000 kW. Larger, more powerful turbines continue to be designed and built.

One of the 50 kW turbines now being developed has a rotor diameter of 14 meters (46 feet). Other 50 kW turbine rotors may be smaller or larger. Towers 30 meters or higher are recommended.

Outdoors, make an outline of a small turbine with either two or three blades. On grass, use yarn kept in place with craft sticks. On asphalt, draw with chalk.

Rotor diameter: 14 m
Tower height: 34 m

* kilowatt or 1000 watts

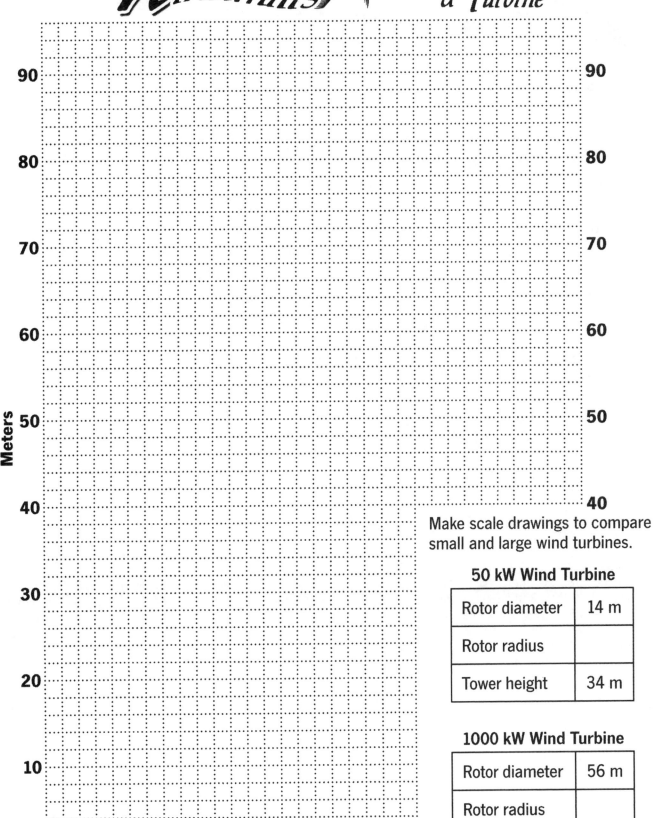

Make scale drawings to compare small and large wind turbines.

50 kW Wind Turbine

Rotor diameter	14 m
Rotor radius	
Tower height	34 m

1000 kW Wind Turbine

Rotor diameter	56 m
Rotor radius	
Tower height	70 m

Windmills — Wind Farm Geography

Key Questions

1. Where are the top ten countries in wind energy use located?
2. Are there wind farms in your state? If so, where are some of them located?
3. In what areas of the United States is it windy enough to consider developing wind farms? Where would wind farms not be a reasonable choice?

Learning Goal

Students will use a variety of resources to find locations that utilize wind energy.

Guiding Documents

Project 2061 Benchmarks

- *Geometric figures, number sequences, graphs, diagrams, sketches, number lines, maps, and stories can be used to represent objects, events, and processes in the real world, although such representations can never be exact in every detail.*
- *Buttress their statements with facts found in books, articles, and databases, and identify the sources used and expect others to do the same.*

NRC Standards

- *Ask a question about objects, organisms, and events in the environment.*
- *Employ simple equipment and tools to gather data and extend the senses.*

National Geography Standards

- *Ask geographic questions—Where is it located? Why is it there? What is significant about its location? How is its location related to the locations of other people, places, and environments?*
- *Locate, gather, and process information from a variety of primary and secondary sources including maps*

Science

Physical science
    wind energy
Environmental science
    renewable resources

Social Science

Geography
    world, country, state

Integrated Processes

Observing
Collecting and recording data
Comparing and contrasting
Interpreting data

Materials

World atlas
World map
Crayons or colored pencils
Internet access

Procedure

After reading *Wind Farms,* do one or more of the following geography activities.

1. Ask the *Key Question,* "Where are the top ten countries in wind energy use located?" Distribute the world map and have students locate and color the countries.
   - On what continents are these countries located?
   - Why do you think other continents are not doing much with wind energy? [maybe lack of wind, lack of money, etc.]
2. Ask the *Key Question,* "Are there wind farms in your state? If so, where are some of them located?" Have students research this data on the Internet. One source:
   http://www.awea.org/projects/index.html
3. Ask the *Key Question,* "In what areas of the United States is it windy enough to consider developing wind farms? Where would wind farms not be a reasonable choice?" Encourage students to find a wind map on the Internet showing annual average wind speeds across the United States.

Connecting Learning

See the questions in *Procedure.*

Windmills

Wind Farm Geography

Color the top ten countries using wind energy.

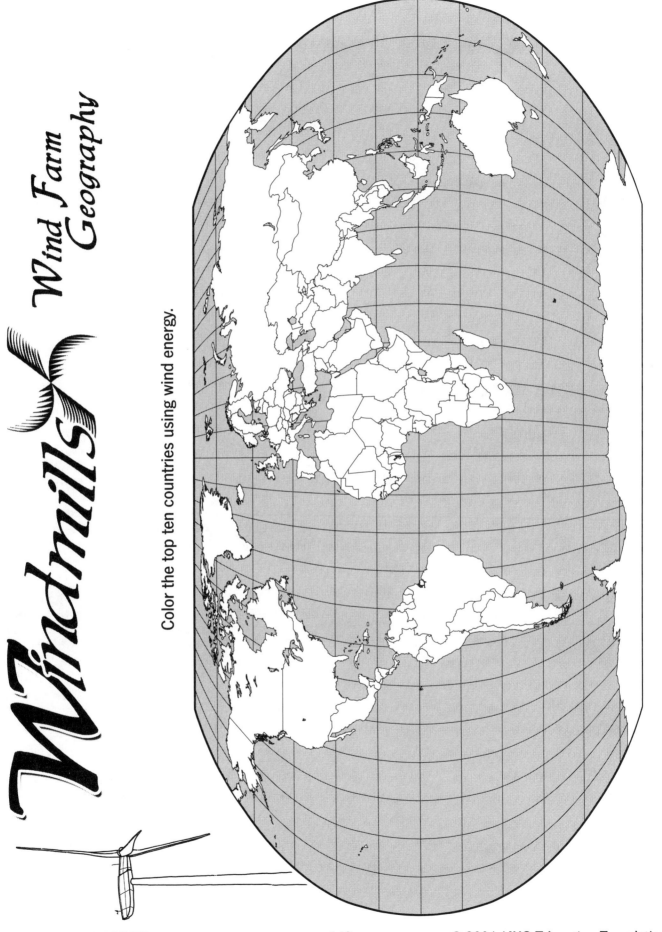

Metal Detector

Topic
Magnetic attraction

Key Question
What do the things that are attracted to our magnet have in common?

Learning Goal
Students will find what things are attracted to a magnet.

Guiding Documents
Project 2061 Benchmark
* *Without touching them, a magnet pulls on all things made of iron and either pushes or pulls on other magnets.*

NRC Standards
* *Objects are made of one or more materials, such as paper, wood, and metal. Objects can be described by the properties of the materials from which they are made, and those properties can be used to separate or sort a group of objects or materials.*
* *Magnets attract and repel each other and certain kinds of other materials.*

Science
Physical science
   magnetism

Integrated Processes
Observing
Classifying
Comparing and contrasting
Generalizing
Inferring

Materials
Large paper grocery bags
Sand
Assorted metallic objects (see *Management 1*)
Ring magnets or cow magnets (see *Management 6*)
Plastic wrap
Pencils or dowels

Background Information
Metals such as iron, cobalt, or nickel (also rare earths and alloys such as steel) are magnetic materials. This means that they can be attracted by magnets, and in some cases even made into magnets. In the atomic structure of these metals, clusters of atoms are aligned magnetically in small areas called magnetic domains. In most magnetic materials, these domains are arranged randomly and they produce no overall magnetic field. However, in the presence of a strong external magnetic field, many of these domains become aligned, allowing a magnet to attract an object made of these metals. If this alignment is permanent, the object becomes a magnet.

Often when asked what things are attracted to magnets, students readily respond with "things made from metal." To help dispel the misconception that any metallic object will be attracted to a magnet, this activity will involve students using a magnet to test various metallic objects: coins, aluminum foil, paper clips, paper fasteners, etc.

All science begins with observations, whether qualitative or quantitative. Observations naturally lead to the making of inferences and predictions.

An inference is an attempt to explain an observation of an event or phenomena. In this activity, students will attempt to explain which metals are attracted to magnets and which are not. Inferences may or may not be scientifically accurate. It is important to probe for the reasoning that underlies the inferences. For instance, students may infer that tin objects are attracted to a magnet because they have observed that the magnet sticks to a "tin can." In reality, the magnet is attracted to the steel that is in the can. In order to alter this incorrect inference, students would need to experience a magnet's reaction to tin.

For further information about magnets and magnetism, refer to *Science Information* in the AIMS publication *Mostly Magnets*.

Management
1. Prior to the activity ask students to bring in small metallic objects. Also have on hand things like paper clips, paper fasteners, aluminum foil, coins, pen caps with metal clasps, etc. If possible, include some magnetic tape from an old audio cassette.
2. Have students work in groups of four.

3. Each group will need a large grocery bag with the top folded down or cut off so that they have a container that is about eight centimeters deep.
4. Add sand to the bag to a depth of about two centimeters. This is their *Bag of Beach* which they will comb for magnetic treasure.
5. The magnets used in this activity are wrapped in plastic wrap for ease of cleaning the iron particles from the sand that are attracted to them.
6. Ring magnets or cow magnets will both work for this activity. Use the stronger cow magnets if they are available. (Both ring magnets and cow magnets can be ordered from AIMS.)

Procedure
1. Ask the students to list the metallic objects their group members brought in. Include, if necessary, items from those you have assembled. Have them predict which items in their collection will be attracted to a magnet.
2. Discuss the similarities of the items students have predicted will be attracted to the magnet.
3. Direct them to bury the objects in the *Bag of Beach*.
4. Inform them that they will be making a "metal detector" out of a magnet to test their predictions.

5. Have students wrap the magnet in a piece of plastic wrap and tie the ends of the plastic wrap around the end of a pencil or dowel.

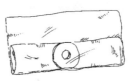 

6. Direct them to hold the metal detector near the surface of the sand to see which objects are attracted to the magnet. (For weaker magnets it may be necessary to either use less sand or to run the metal detector through the sand.)
7. Ask students to classify their objects into two groups, attracted by the magnet and not attracted by the magnet.
8. Have them compare their results to their predictions.
9. Discuss the similarities of the objects that were attracted to the magnets.
10. Encourage students to form a generalization about objects that are attracted to magnets. [Not all metallic objects are attracted to magnets. Only some metals are attracted to magnets.]
11. Have students bury their objects in the sand once again and trade bags with another group. Encourage them to use the metal detector once again. Ask if they were surprised about their results this time.

Connecting Learning
1. When you made your first predictions, what kind of objects did you think would be attracted to the magnet?
2. Were you surprised or puzzled by your results?
3. How did you have to change what you thought about magnetic objects?
4. Do you think our metal detector would be good for finding hidden treasure? Explain.
5. Why shouldn't our device be called a metal detector? [It doesn't detect all metals; it only attracts objects with magnetic properties.] What would be a better name?
6. What other objects would you like to try?
7. Why did we wrap the magnet in plastic wrap? [to make the iron particles from the sand easier to remove from the magnet]
8. To find out what metals are attracted to a magnet, what other tests could we do?
9. What are you wondering now?

Extension
See *Mostly Magnets* for more activities dealing with magnets and magnetism.

151

Metal Detector

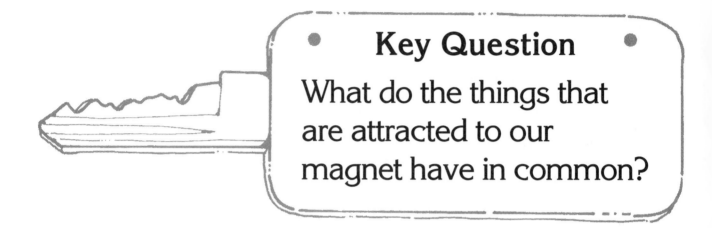

Key Question

What do the things that are attracted to our magnet have in common?

Learning Goal

Students will:

- find what things are attracted to a magnet.

Metal Detector

Wrap the magnet in plastic wrap.

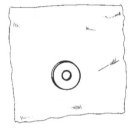 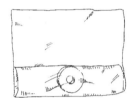 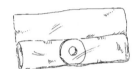 

Tie the ends of the plastic wrap around the end of your pencil.

List the objects hidden in your "bag of beach."

Check (√) the ones you predict will be attracted by the magnet.

Now comb the beach for the treasure.

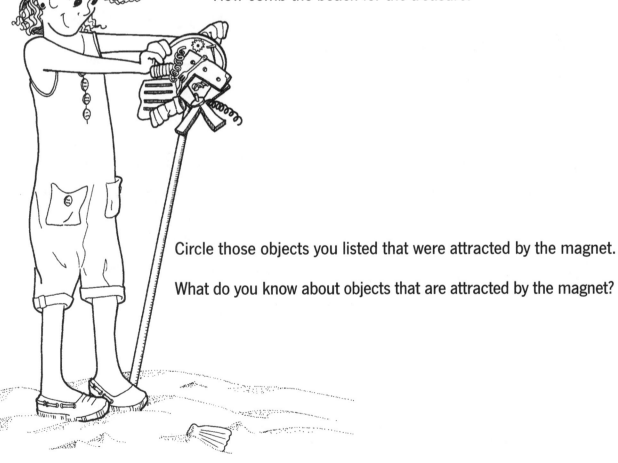

Circle those objects you listed that were attracted by the magnet.

What do you know about objects that are attracted by the magnet?

153 © 2004 AIMS Education Foundation

Metal Detector

1. When you made your first predictions, what kind of objects did you think would be attracted to the magnet?

2. Were you surprised or puzzled by your results? Explain.

3. How did you have to change what you thought about magnetic objects?

4. Do you think our metal detector would be good for finding hidden treasure? Explain.

5. Why shouldn't our device be called a metal detector? What would be a better name?

6. What other objects would you like to try?

7. Why did we wrap the magnet in plastic wrap?

8. To find out what metals are attracted to a magnet, what other tests could we do?

9. What are you wondering now?

Static Sensations

Topic
Static electric force

Key Question
How can you use your senses to experience the static electric force?

Learning Goal
Students will explore and experience the static electric force using their senses of feeling, hearing, and seeing.

Guiding Documents
Project 2061 Benchmark
- *Without touching them, material that has been electrically charged pulls on all other materials and may either push or pull other charged materials.*

NRC Standard
- *The behavior of individual organisms is influenced by internal cues (such as hunger) and by external cues (such as a change in the environment). Humans and other organisms have senses that help them detect internal and external cues.*

Science
Physical science
　force
　　static electricity
Life science
　senses

Integrated Processes
Observing
Comparing and contrasting
Collecting and recording data

Materials
Rubber balloons, one per student
Paper clips, one per student
Fluorescent bulb (see *Management 6*)
Student pages

Background Information
　Static electricity is a normal part of our everyday world, yet we rarely think of it as a force. In fact, static electricity is one manifestation of a fundamental force in the universe—the electromagnetic force. Some of the key properties of this fundamental force, in its static electricity form, can be easily observed by elementary school students using their senses of feeling, hearing, and seeing.

　One of the key characteristics of the static electric force is that it is able to act at a distance and make things move without coming in direct contact with them. In addition, this force both attracts and repels, depending, respectively, on whether unlike or like charges are involved. In these two important ways, this force is very different from the normal pushing and pulling forces we encounter in our everyday experience.

Management
1. This activity has three main parts and an optional fourth part. All four parts can be completed in one class period. Each part can be done with the whole class or in small groups. In either case, students need their own balloons so that they can experience the static electric force firsthand.
2. This activity works best in cool, dry conditions.
3. Balloons should be inflated ahead of time. Balloons that are inflated close to their maximum size produce a better static charge than under-inflated balloons.
4. Balloons can be charged by rubbing them on students' hair or clothing. Not all materials will charge the balloons equally, however. For example, clothing containing nylon or wool will work better than cotton clothing.
5. The fourth part of this activity is optional. If you choose to do it, you will need to get a fluorescent bulb and let students take turns lighting it with their charged balloons. The darker the room, the easier it is to see the faint light produced when the bulb is lit by the static discharge.
6. Any kind of fluorescent lightbulb will work, but the tube bulbs like those in most classrooms work best.

Procedure
Part One
1. Distribute the balloons and the first activity sheet.
2. Ask the question: "*How can you use your sense of feeling to experience the static electric force?*"
3. Demonstrate how to charge the balloons by stroking them on your hair or clothing.
4. Have students follow the directions on the student sheet. After they do each part, lead them in a discussion and have them record their answers.

Part Two
1. Give students the second activity sheet.
2. Ask the question: *How can you use your sense of hearing to experience the static electric force?*
3. Have students follow the directions on the second student sheet. After they do each part, lead them in a discussion and have them record their answers.

Part Three
1. Distribute the third activity sheet.
2. Ask the question: *How can you use your sense of seeing to experience the static electric force?*
3. Have students follow the directions on the student sheet. After they do each part, lead them in a discussion and have them record their answers.
4. Conclude the activity with a whole-class discussion that focuses on how students used their various senses to observe the static electric force in various ways. If appropriate, discuss the static electric force in greater detail.

Part Four
1. Give students the fourth activity sheet.
2. Ask the question: *What happens when you bring your charged balloon near the electrodes of a fluorescent light bulb?*
3. Put out a fluorescent bulb and turn off the classroom lights. Let students take turns lighting the bulb by charging their balloons and then letting them discharge on the bulb electrodes. Multiple discharges are possible by rotating different parts of the balloon near the electrodes.

Connecting Learning
Part One
1. What did you notice when you moved the charged balloon just above the back of your hand? [Students should feel a tingling as the static charge attracts the hairs on the backs of their hands.]
2. What did you notice when you moved the charged balloon just above the palm of your hand? [Students will not likely feel any sensation since there are no hairs on the palms of their hands.]
3. What did you notice when you moved the balloon around your head? [Students will notice the charge in some areas more than others.]

Part Two
1. What did you hear when you brought a paper clip near your charged balloon? [Depending on the amount of charge, students will hear either faint or strong crackles as the static charge jumps to the paper clip.]
2. What did you hear when you brought other objects close to your charged balloon? [Depending on material, students will either hear crackling or not hear anything. The crackling only occurs when the static charge jumps across an air gap, and this will only happen with certain materials—the better conducting the material, the more likely it is to hear the crackle.]
3. What can you tell about the static electric force from this experience? [Static electricity can be observed by hearing it. The static electricity makes a crackling sound as it jumps across to the paper clip. The crackling sound can be heard with some materials, but not others.]

Part Three
1. What did you see when you lowered your charged balloon over the page? [The paper was attracted and pulled up to the balloon.]
2. What did you notice when you brought the balloon near various other materials? [Most light objects move and attach themselves to the charged balloon. Although the balloon also attracts heavier objects, the static electric force isn't able to overcome the gravitational force and pick them up.]
3. What happened when you held your charged balloon next to the wall and let go? [The balloon stuck to the wall.]

Part Four
1. What did you see when you brought your charged balloon near the electrodes of the fluorescent bulb? [The static electricity discharged and lit the bulb.]
2. What did you notice when you brought various parts of the balloon near the electrodes? [There were multiple discharges that lit up the bulb.]
3. Forces often move things. In this activity, what moved? [the electric charge in the form of electrons that jumped from the balloon to the electrodes]
4. Lightning is a powerful example of static electricity in nature. How is this investigation like lightning and how is it different? *[Alike:* Both are discharges of static electricity. In both, electric charges move rapidly from one area to another. Both produce sound and light. *Different:* Lightning is much more dangerous and powerful. The thunder caused by lightning is much louder than the crackle created as a balloon discharges. Lightning can be observed with the sense of smell; it ionizes the air, creating a distinctive odor.]
5. What have you learned about the static electric force from all four parts of this activity? [The static electric force acts at a distance. The static force attracts various small objects. The static charge can be observed using the senses of feeling, hearing, and seeing.]
6. What are you wondering now?

Extensions
1. Have students experiment with other ways to charge the balloons.
2. Have students charge other materials, like plastic wrap, and see if they can notice a difference between these materials and the balloon.
3. In the examples used in this activity, the static force always attracts. Have students try to create a situation in which the static force repels.
4. Lightning is nature's static electric light and sound show. Students can research lightning and write a report on it.
5. See the AIMS book, *Electrical Connections,* for more activities dealing with electricity.

Static Sensations

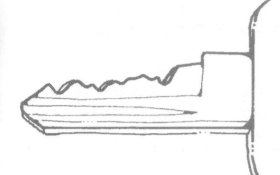

Key Question

How can you use your senses to experience the static electric force?

Learning Goal

Students will:

- explore and experience the static electric force using their senses of feeling, hearing, and seeing.

Static Sensations

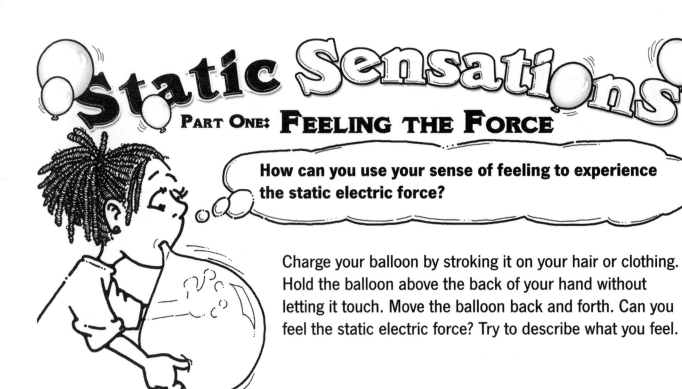

PART ONE: FEELING THE FORCE

How can you use your sense of feeling to experience the static electric force?

Charge your balloon by stroking it on your hair or clothing. Hold the balloon above the back of your hand without letting it touch. Move the balloon back and forth. Can you feel the static electric force? Try to describe what you feel.

Charge the balloon again and move it just above the palm of your hand without letting it touch. What do you notice this time?

Charge the balloon once more and try to feel the static charge by holding the balloon near various parts of your face and head. Describe what you discover.

In this first part of the activity you have used your sense of feeling to experience the static electric force. This force is able to act at a distance without making direct contact with an object. How did this experiment demonstrate this?

What else can you say about the static force from this experience?

Static Sensations
PART TWO: HEARING THE FORCE

How can you use your sense of hearing to experience the static electric force?

Charge your balloon and hold it in one hand. With your other hand, slowly bring a paper clip close to the charged part of the balloon (the part that was rubbed). Move the paper clip back and forth over the charged surface of the balloon without letting it touch. What do you hear when you do this?

Charge the balloon again and slowly bring other objects close to the balloon. What do you hear?

In this second part, you have used your sense of hearing to experience the static electric force. What can you tell about the static electric force from this experience?

PART THREE: SEEING THE FORCE

How can you use your sense of seeing to experience the static electric force?

Charge your balloon. Slowly lower your balloon over this page. What do you see when you do this?

Charge the balloon again and slowly bring it near a variety of other objects. What do you see?

Charge the balloon once more and let it touch the wall. Let go of the balloon. What do you see?

In this third part, you have used your sense of seeing to experience the static electric force. What have you learned about the static electric force from all three parts of this activity?

Static Sensations

PART FOUR: AN ENLIGHTENING EXPERIENCE

What happens when you bring your charged balloon near the electrodes of a fluorescent light bulb?

electrodes < **fluorescent bulb**

Charge your balloon and slowly bring it near the electrodes on the bulb. Be sure to bring various parts of the balloon near the electrodes. What do you observe?

Forces often move things. In this activity, what moved?

In what ways is this activity is similar to lightning and in what ways is it different?

Summary:
What did you learn about the static electric force in all four parts of this activity?

161

Static Sensations

Part One

1. What did you notice when you moved the charged balloon just above the back of your hand?

2. What did you notice when you moved the charged balloon just above the palm of your hand?

3. What did you notice when you moved the balloon around your head?

Part Two

1. What did you hear when you brought a paper clip near your charged balloon?

2. What did you hear when you brought other objects close to your charged balloon?

3. What can you tell about the static electric force from this experience?

Part Three

1. What did you see when you lowered your charged balloon over the page?

2. What did you notice when you brought the balloon near various other materials?

3. What happened when you held your charged balloon next the wall and let go?

Part Four

1. What did you see when you brought your charged balloon near the electrodes of the fluorescent bulb?

2. What did you notice when you brought various parts of the balloon near the electrodes?

3. Forces often move things. In this activity, what moved?

4. Lightning is a powerful example of static electricity in nature. How is this investigation like lightning and how is it different?

5. What have you learned about the static electric force from all four parts of this activity?

Meter Readers

Topic
Energy conservation: electric meters

Key Question
How much electricity does your family use from day to day?

Learning Goals
Students will:
- become aware of their electrical energy consumption by reading their home electric meters, and
- learn ways to conserve.

Guiding Documents
Project 2061 Benchmarks
- *People try to conserve energy in order to slow down the depletion of energy resources and/or to save money.*
- *Graphical display of numbers may make it possible to spot patterns that are not otherwise obvious, such as comparative size and trends.*

NRC Standard
- *The supply of many resources is limited. If used, resources can be extended through recycling and decreased use.*

NCTM Standards 2000*
- *Collect data using observations, surveys, and experiments*
- *Represent data using tables and graphs such as line plots, bar graphs, and line graphs*

Math
Place value
Whole number operations
    subtraction
Bar graph

Science
Physical science
    electricity
Environmental science
    conservation

Integrated Processes
Observing
Controlling variables
Collecting and recording data
Comparing and contrasting
Interpreting data
Relating

Materials
Electric meter at home
Scissors
6" x 18" construction paper, one per student
Paper fasteners, five per student

Background Information
It was in the 1880s that electricity first became available for homes and work places—but only in large cities such as New York and London. It was mainly used for lighting. By the 1930s, electricity was more readily available. The first successful electric meter was made in 1888. A watt-hour meter, the basis for the kind used now, was patented in 1895.

Electricity is brought from the source where it is generated through wires attached to tall poles. Wires branch off from these main wires and go to each house. They may be above ground or underground. At a house, the wires split into several different circuits.

The electric meter records the amount of energy used by all the electrical circuits in a building. The energy is measured in kilowatt-hours, 1000 watts of power for one hour of time. The formula for kilowatt-hours is (watts x hours)/1000.

There is increasing concern about conserving electricity, both for financial reasons and because the supply of electricity is limited. The amount of electricity used is affected by *climate*; hot summers, for example, trigger the need for air conditioning. *The number of persons in a household* affects the amount of hot water needed for bathing and washing clothes as well as the use of cooking appliances. *Personal diligence* in turning off unneeded lights, decreasing hot water use, buying energy-efficient appliances, and adjusting the thermostat contributes to conservation efforts.

Management
1. To demonstrate how to read the meter, make a sample *Meter Model* and a transparency of the *Electric Meter* page.
2. Decide the span of time for data gathering, preferably a week but a minimum of four days.

For students ready for more independent work:

> *Guided Planning:* Ask the *Key Question* and give groups the *Plan* page to organize their own investigations. Use the *Electric Meter* page and the *Meter Model* to acquaint the class with reading the meter.

Procedure

First Day

1. Ask the *Key Question:* How much electricity does your family use from day to day?
2. Distribute the *Meter Model* page, construction paper, and paper fasteners. After students make the models, read the *Electric Meter* page. Invite students to set the models and practice reading.
3. Give students the *Data* page and have them record the date for the first reading. To facilitate subtraction, have students start recording on the last line of the table and go upward from there.
4. Instruct students to gather data at the same time each day, the controlled variable. On the first and last days, ask them to also draw the position of the dial pointers on the upper half of the page.

Subsequent Days

1. After the first reading, resolve any questions that arise. Suggest student peers check the accuracy by comparing the first reading to the drawn meter.
2. When data-gathering is completed, have students calculate the *Difference* column and the total kilowatt-hours used (last day minus first day). Urge capable students to find the average (mean) per day.
3. Give students the *Graph* page and guide them in constructing the bar graph with these questions:
   - What labels do we need? [date (horizontal axis), kilowatt-hours (vertical axis), and a graph title]
   - What shall we "count by" to label the kilowatt hours? (probably ones, twos, or fives, depending on the range of data)
4. Instruct students to complete their graphs, study the results, and write statements about the information. Discuss.

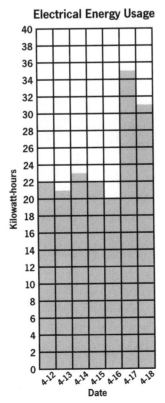

Connecting Learning

1. Why are the pointers on the meter dials usually *between* two numbers rather than on a number?
2. What if data were gathered at 4 P.M. one day and 7 P.M. the next day? [It isn't fair to compare time periods of different lengths.]
3. How much electricity does your family use? Do you think it will be about the same next week? Explain.
4. Were there any days where your use of electricity went up more than others? If so, why do you think so? [laundry day, baking day, a particularly hot or cold day, etc.]
5. How can we find the cost of the electricity used? [The utility bill gives the cost per kilowatt-hour. Multiply by the number of kwh.]
6. What might cause differences in the electricity used from family to family? [number of people in household, how carefully they try to conserve, the number and energy efficiency of large electrical appliances such as refrigerators, size of the home (a larger place takes more energy to heat or cool), home insulation, etc.]
7. How does weather affect electrical use? [Heating in winter and air conditioning in summer use a major amount of energy. The more severe the weather, the more energy is needed to make people comfortable.]
8. In what ways are you and your family trying to save electricity at home? ...at school?
9. What are you wondering now?

Curriculum Correlation

Literature

Berger, Melvin. *Switch On, Switch Off.* HarperCollins. New York. 1989. (This book traces the flow of electricity from a generator to the lamp in your home with easy-to-understand explanations and helpful illustrations. Its usefulness extends beyond the K-3 designation.)

Art

Have students design posters about ways to save electricity.

Home Link

Encourage students, together with their parents, to keep personal records of the information on their utility bill for several months. With parents' consent, the records, a graph, and conclusions could be turned in for extra credit.

Meter Readers

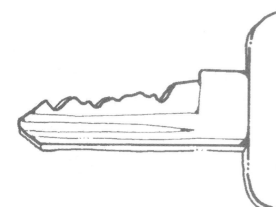

Key Question

How much electricity does your family use from day to day?

Learning Goals

Students will:

- become aware of their electrical energy consumption by reading their home electric meters, and
- learn ways to conserve.

Plan

How much electricity does your family use from day to day?

1. What kinds of data are needed? How will you record the data?

2. Where can the data be found?

3. What variable needs to be controlled?

4. For how many days will data be gathered?

5. How will you show the results?

6. After seeing the results, what new questions do you have?

Meter Model

Cut and glue the meters on construction paper.
Cut and attach the pointers with paper fasteners.

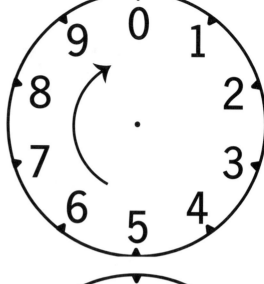

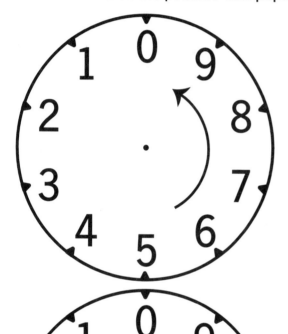

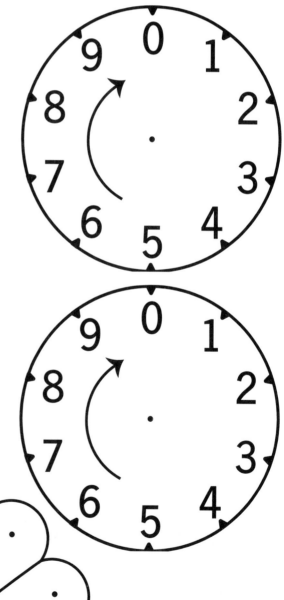

Electric Meter

The electric meter measures the amount of energy used during a particular time period. The energy is measured in kilowatt-hours (kWh), 1000 watt-hours. A kilowatt-hour is equal to ten 100-watt bulbs burning for one hour. The cost of a kilowatt-hour depends on the kind of fuel used to generate electricity and the cost of delivering it.

A meter records the energy used by all the electrical circuits in your home. Older homes may have four dials that turn over to zero after every 1000 kWh. Due to the large amounts of electricity needed for air conditioners and an increasing number of appliances, newer homes have five dials that return to zero after every 10,000 kWh. Some of the newest meters are digital.

| ten-thousands | thousands | hundreds | tens | ones |

Notice that some dials move in a clockwise direction and other dials in a counter-clockwise direction. When the pointer is between two numbers, record the number it has just passed.

Professional meter readers look at the position of the pointers, rather than the numbers, much like you read a clock. They can generally read up to 20 feet away, 150 feet with binoculars. A computer will reject their reading if it does not compare with past usage.

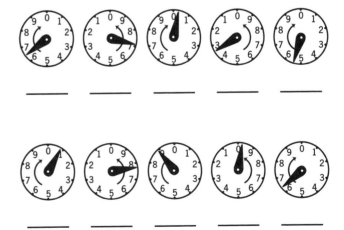

____ ____ ____ ____ ____

____ ____ ____ ____ ____

Data

How much electricity does your family use from day to day?

Read your electric meter at the same time each day. On the first and last days you take readings, draw the position of each dial pointer.

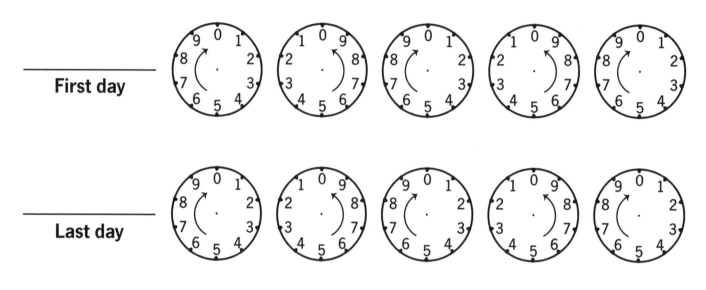

_____ **First day**

_____ **Last day**

Total difference: _____ kWh

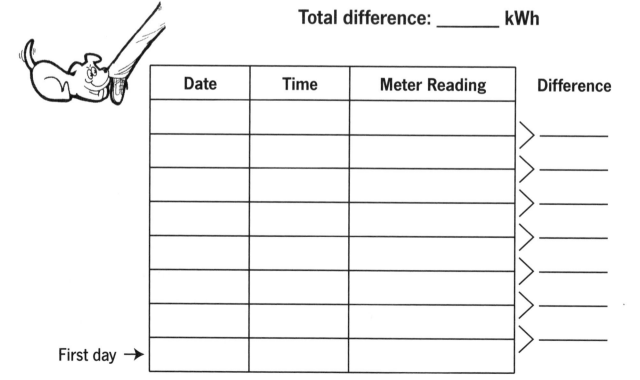

Date	Time	Meter Reading	Difference
			>_____
			>_____
			>_____
			>_____
			>_____
			>_____
			>_____
			>_____

First day →

Graph

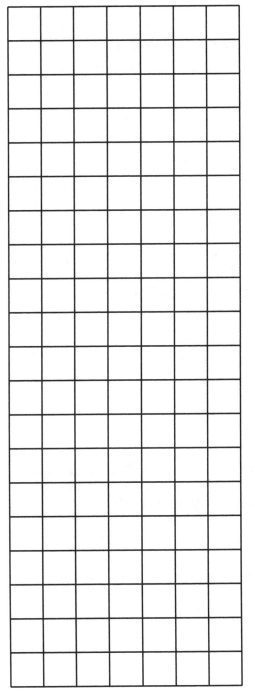

Construct a bar graph to show the electricity your family used each day.

What does the graph tell you?
Write at least two statements.

Meter Readers

1. Why are the pointers on the meter dials usually *between* two numbers rather than on a number?

2. What if data were gathered at 4 P.M. one day and 7 P.M. the next day?

3. What have you learned from your graph?

4. How much electricity does your family use? Do you think it will be about the same next week? Explain.

5. Were there any days where your use of electricity went up more than others? If so, why do you think so?

6. How can we find the cost of the electricity used?

7. What might cause differences in the electricity used from family to family?

8. How does weather affect electrical usage?

9. In what ways are you and your family trying to save electricity?

10. What are you wondering now?

Topic
Energy conservation: appliances

Key Question
How does the electrical energy appliances use compare?

Learning Goals
Students will:
- become aware of the number of watts used by various household appliances, and
- use this information to think about energy conservation.

Guiding Documents
Project 2061 Benchmark
- *People try to conserve energy in order to slow down the depletion of energy resources and/or save money.*

NRC Standard
- *The supply of many resources is limited. If used, resources can be extended through recycling and decreased use.*

NCTM Standards 2000*
- *Collect data using observations, surveys, and experiments*
- *Recognize and apply mathematics in contexts outside of mathematics*

Math
Whole number operations
Ordering

Science
Physical science
  electricity
Environmental science
  conservation

Integrated Processes
Observing
Predicting
Collecting and recording data
Comparing and contrasting
Relating

Materials
Appliances at home
Hair dryer or other small appliance

Background Information
Watts are a unit of electrical energy. Scientifically speaking, one watt is equal to one joule of energy per second or when one ampere of current is produced by one volt. Utility companies measure electrical energy in kilowatt-hours (kWh), equivalent to the power supplied by 1000 watts for one hour.

Sometimes appliance energy information is given in amps but no volts are listed. In the United States, regular household circuits are 120 volts. Appliances with high wattages, such as the clothes dryer and the range/oven, will be on a 240-volt circuit. The actual number of volts delivered on a circuit varies. For example, a 120-volt circuit may range between 110 and 125 volts.

The energy needed to operate home appliances is increasingly expensive. Energy-efficient appliances can save considerable money over the life of the appliance. *Energy Guide Labels* that list the yearly cost per kwh are required for all new refrigerators, freezers, water heaters, clothes washers, dishwashers, and room air conditioners. The expected lifetime of most large appliances varies from 12 to 20 years. This means a $700 refrigerator using $90 of energy per year, will cost $2500 over 20 years.

The biggest users of energy are the central heating/cooling system, water heater, and the refrigerator/freezer. It is helpful to lower the thermostat for heating and raise it for cooling. Short showers use significantly less hot water than baths, saving energy needed to heat the water.

But even the cost of using lights can add up to $50-$150 a year. Fluorescent bulbs are three to four times more efficient than incandescent bulbs and last about 10 times longer.

Electrical Energy Efficiency

Per Use	Cost[1]
Electric clothes dryer	$ .29
Electric clothes washer	$ .21
Electric dishwasher	$ .35
Electric blanket, per night	$ .07
Vacuum cleaner	$ .07
Blow dryer (hair)	$ .04

Per Day	
Electric water heater with blanket	
5 people in household	$1.90
4 people in household	$1.56
3 people in household	$1.22
2 people in household	$ .88
Refrigerator	
18 cubic ft (pre 1992)[2]	$ .37
19 cubic ft (1992 or later)	$ .27
24 cubic ft (1992 or later)	$ .30
Satellite dish	$ .02

Kwh Per Hour	
Central Air Conditioner	
3-ton (1500 sq ft house)	$ .48
4-ton (2000 sq ft house)	$ .64
5-ton (2000 sq ft house)	$ .44
1100-watt room air conditioner	$ .11
Evaporative cooler	$ .05
Whole house fan (.5 horsepower)	$ .05
Portable heater	$ .15
Electric oven	$ .23
Electric rangetop burner	$ .13
Microwave	$ .15
Toaster oven	$ .12
Electric frying pan	$ .10
Color television	$ .01
2 HP pool filter	$ .20
Home computer	$ .02

1. Averages based on 10 cents per kWh, adjusted from Pacific Gas and Electric website data at www.pge.com.
2. In 1992, a new law set minimum standards of energy efficiency for many major appliances, including refrigerators.

Management

For those students ready for more independent work, ask the *Key Question* and have students plan their own investigation. For direct comparison, explain how to convert amps and volts or kilowatts into watts. Questions that may help with planning:

- What appliances will you investigate?
- Make a prediction of energy usage by ordering the chosen appliances from highest to lowest.
- How will you find the electrical energy data?
- What measuring unit will be used to compare the appliances?
- What are group responsibilities? ...individual responsibilities? (Example: Plan as a group, but investigate individually.)
- How will you record the results?
- After carrying out the plan, what conclusions and questions do you have?
- How can you better conserve electricity?

Procedure

1. Ask students to name some electrical appliances at their homes, both large and small.
2. Distribute the first activity page and direct student attention to the appliances listed in the table. Have students write their prediction about which use the most watts per hour, ordering appliances from highest to lowest.
3. Give students the picture page to take home, complete, and return the next day. Tell students to look for a sticker or plate on the outside of the appliance, on the edge of a door, or on an interior wall. Demonstrate how to locate and record data, using the hair dryer.

   Emphasize that students are searching for the number of watts. If watts are not listed, have students look for amps and volts or kilowatts. Later this data will be converted into watts so the appliances can be compared.
4. The next day, have students transfer the data to the table. They will fill either the amps and volts columns, the kilowatts column, or the watts column, depending on the data available for a given appliance.
5. Guide students in using the formulas to complete the watts column.
6. Instruct students to order the appliances by actual number of watts and compare with their predictions.
7. Discuss the results and brainstorm ways to conserve.

Connecting Learning

1. Which home appliances use the most electrical energy per hour? [probably the clothes dryer and range] Did everyone find this to be true?
2. What other home appliances might be big energy users? [central heater or furnace, air conditioner, and water heater]
3. Watts *and* hours of use determine which appliances use the most energy. Which appliances do you think use the most electricity during the year? [central heater or furnace, central air conditioner, water heater, refrigerator/freezer, etc. According to one recent statistic, refrigerators alone use about 7% of the electricity in the United States.]
4. How does weather affect electrical use? [Heating in winter and air conditioning in summer use a major amount of energy. The more severe the weather, the greater the energy used.]
5. In what ways are you already trying to save electricity at home? ...at school?
6. What are you wondering now?

Extensions

1. Convert watts into kilowatts (watts ÷ 1000), and complete the kilowatt column of the table. Using local kilowatt-hour rates, compute the cost of running each appliance for one hour. Record costs in a column added to the table.
2. On the Internet, search for energy data on appliances and conservation tips.

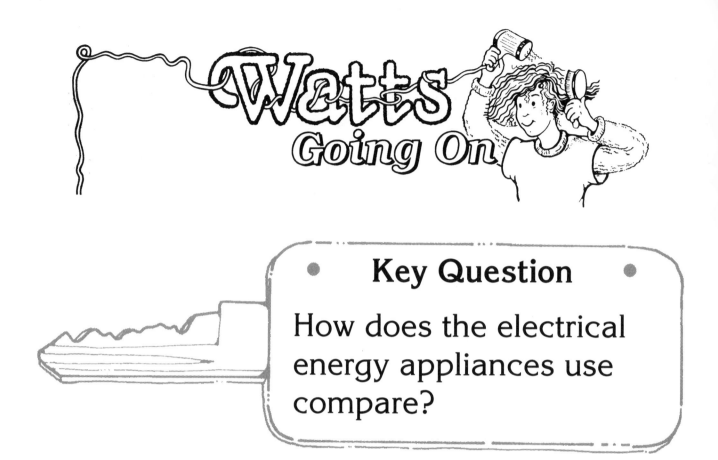

Watts Going On

Key Question

How does the electrical energy appliances use compare?

Learning Goals

Students will:

- become aware of the number of watts used by various household appliances, and
- use this information to think about energy conservation.

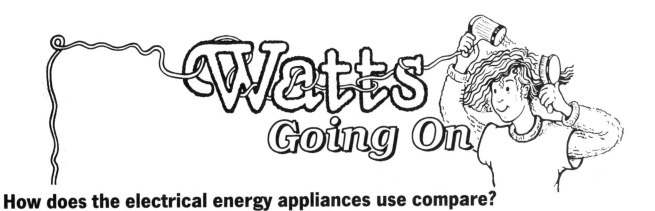

Watts Going On

How does the electrical energy appliances use compare?

	Prediction (highest to lowest)	Actual

For direct comparison, calculate the number of watts for these appliances.
The following formulas can be used where watts are not listed.

amps x volts = watts   kilowatts x 1000 = watts

(watts ÷ 1000)

Appliance	Amps	Volts	Watts	Kilowatts
Clothes dryer				
Hair dryer				
Iron				
Microwave				
Range/oven				
Refrigerator				
Television				
Vacuum cleaner				

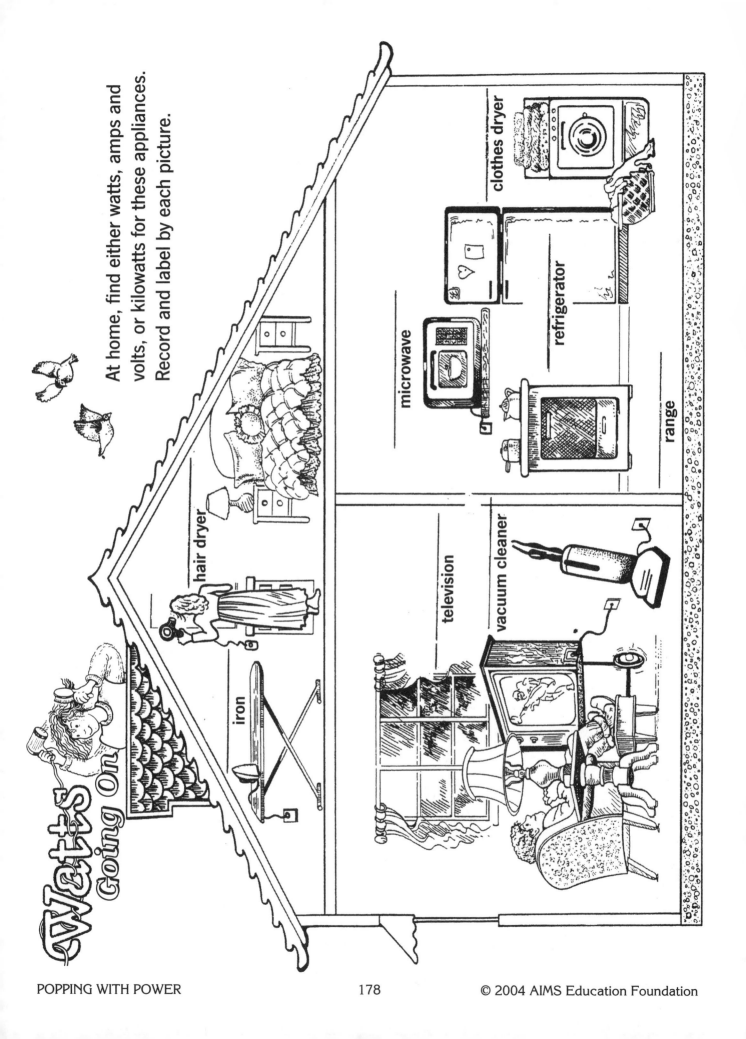

Watts Going On

At home, find either watts, amps and volts, or kilowatts for these appliances. Record and label by each picture.

hair dryer

iron

clothes dryer

microwave

refrigerator

range

television

vacuum cleaner

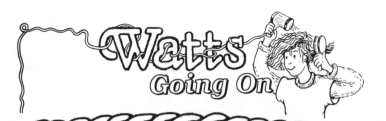

1. Which home appliances use the most electrical energy per hour? Did everyone find this to be true?

2. What other home appliances might be big energy users?

3. Watts *and* hours of use determine which appliances use the most energy. Which appliances do you think use the most electricity during the year?

4. How does weather affect electrical use?

5. In what ways are you already trying to save electricity at home?

6. How can we save electricity at school?

7. What are you wondering now?

Topic
Energy conservation: light bulbs

Key Questions
1. Do you live in a 3000-watt house?
2. How can the energy used to light your house be reduced?

Learning Goals
Students will:
- become aware of the number of watts used in the light bulbs in their homes, and
- think about ways to conserve energy.

Guiding Documents
Project 2061 Benchmarks
- *Some energy sources cost less than others and some cause less pollution than others.*
- *People try to conserve energy in order to slow down the depletion of energy resources and/or save money.*

NRC Standard
- *The supply of many resources is limited. If used, resources can be extended through recycling and decreased use.*

NCTM Standards 2000*
- *Collect data using observations, surveys, and experiments*
- *Recognize and apply mathematics in contexts outside of mathematics*

Math
Whole number operations
    addition, multiplication, division
Decimals
Estimation
    rounding
Graph
    bar

Science
Physical science
    electricity
Environmental science
    conservation

Integrated Processes
Observing
Comparing and contrasting
Collecting and recording data
Interpreting data
Relating

Materials
Light bulbs at home

Background Information
An incandescent bulb generates a great amount of heat to produce light. Only 5-8% of the energy produced is converted into light; the rest is dispersed as heat. The number of lumens determines the brightness of the light. The higher the number of lumens per watt, the higher the filament temperature and the whiter the light. The tungsten filament heats to temperatures of 2000-2500°C (3600-4500°F), turning it white-hot. Incandescent bulbs burn out because the filament weakens from being repeatedly heated to high temperatures and then cooled.

In a fluorescent bulb, electricity from a magnetic or electronic ballast causes the gases in the bulb to glow with ultraviolet light, making the bulb's phosphorus coating also glow. Fluorescent bulbs, although initially more expensive, make up the cost in energy savings. They can generate the same number of lumens as an incandescent bulb at a significantly reduced wattage. Manufacturer's claims for fluorescent equivalents vary, for example, from 23 to 28 watts for a 100-watt incandescent bulb. Measured by lumens or brightness, the 28-watt fluorescent bulb is considered the true equivalent.

Another benefit is that fluorescent bulbs have a relatively long life. It takes about ten incandescent bulbs to equal the life of one fluorescent bulb.

Replacing incandescent bulbs with fluorescent bulbs is one way to save energy used for lighting. In fact, some city ordinances require fluorescent bulbs in certain parts of new homes and utility companies are encouraging their use. Another way to conserve is to be diligent in turning off unneeded lights.

Management
1. The first part of the activity revolves around taking a home survey of light bulbs. The second part deals with learning about both incandescent and fluorescent bulbs, followed by calculating and comparing respective energy costs per hour.

2. Caution students to count only the light bulbs in sockets, preferably when they are turned off. Do not count bulbs being stored for future use.
3. Advise students to ask for their parents' help in determining the watts in ceiling fixtures. If unobtainable, a family visit to a store to read the wattage labels of similar bulbs may be helpful. Standard 4-foot fluorescent tubes are generally 32 or 40 watts.
4. Research or have students research the local utility rate for kilowatt-hours (kWh) on a recent bill or through the Internet. This activity focuses primarily on the energy-saving aspect.

For those students ready for more independent work:

> *Open-ended:* Ask the *Key Questions* and have students plan how they will collect, record, and display the data. Fur further information, distribute the *Incandescent versus Fluorescent* page.

Procedure

Part One: Home Survey

1. Ask the first *Key Question:* "Do you live in a 3000-watt house?" Distribute the first activity page.
2. Instruct students to circle the estimate of their total light bulb wattage.
3. Ask, "What kind of data do we need to record?" [kind of bulb, wattage, and number of bulbs] "How could the data be organized?" (Take suggestions that students can then implement.) Discuss any questions students may have about conducting the survey.
4. Have students complete the survey at home and bring it back to school.

Part Two: Saving Energy

1. Together with students, study the *Incandescent versus Fluorescent* page.
2. Give students the last activity page with the question, "How can the energy used to light your house be reduced?" Record their initial suggestions on the board or chart paper for further discussion later.
3. Guide students in transferring data from their surveys into the *Home Survey* table.
4. Have students compute the total watts column and then the grand total.
5. Explain that utility companies measure electrical energy in kilowatt-hours (kWh), equivalent to the power supplied by 1000 watts for one hour. Have students discuss how to calculate the number of kilowatts and also the cost per hour if all the lights are on. Round decimals to the nearest cent (hundredth).

grand total watts ÷ 1000 = kilowatts
kilowatts x $. _ _ (local rate) = cost per hour

I = incandescent
F = fluorescent

Home Survey

Kind	Watts	# of bulbs	Total watts
I	100 w	12	1200
I	75 w	5	375
I	60 w	14	840
F	40 w	6	240
Grand total			2655
Kilowatts			2.66
Cost per hour			$ .27*

All Fluorescents

Watts	# of bulbs	Total watts
28 w	12	336
20 w	5	100
15 w	14	210
40 w	6	240
Grand total		886
Kilowatts		0.89
Cost per hour		$ .09*

* at 10¢ per kwh

6. Direct students to change all their bulbs in the survey to equivalent fluorescent bulbs and complete the table calculations. Any fluorescent bulbs already in their surveys should be transferred over to the next table also.
7. As a class, determine the increments for the *Cents* label, probably ones or twos, and have students finish the graph.
8. Through class discussion, have students interpret their data and refine the list of energy-saving suggestions recorded earlier. Instruct them to write two suggestions on their paper.

Connecting Learning

1. What problems, if any, did you have getting the light bulb information? How can these problems be solved?
2. Which light bulb wattage was most common at your house? Which wattage was most common in all our houses?
3. Where do you need brighter lights? Where do you need dimmer lights?
4. How many light bulb watts are used in your house?
5. What is a kilowatt? How can we find our energy rate per kilowatt-hour?
6. If all the lights were on, how much would it cost per hour?
7. Which computations did you do mentally? ...on paper? ...with a calculator? Explain your choices.
8. In what ways can you save electricity?
9. What are you wondering now?

Extensions

1. Wearing gloves, carefully break open a used incandescent bulb so students can examine the circuit structure.
2. Search the Internet for more energy conservation information about lighting.

* Reprinted with permission from *Principles and Standards for School Mathematics,* 2000 by the National Council of Teachers of Mathematics. All rights reserved.

Lighten Up

Key Questions

1. Do you live in a 3000-watt house?
2. How can the energy used to light your house be reduced?

Learning Goals

Students will:

- become aware of the number of watts used in the light bulbs in their homes, and
- examine ways to conserve energy.

Do you live in a 3000-watt house?

Circle the number of estimated light bulb watts in your house.

Below 1000

1000s

2000s

3000s

4000s

Light bulb home survey
Record the kind of bulb (incandescent or fluorescent) and the number
of bulbs of each wattage in lamps and ceiling fixtures.

Incandescent
versus Fluorescent

filament

Incandescent bulbs
Current travels through a circuit, heating the filament to a white hot glow. Light is produced by heat. Incandescent bulbs produce about 15 lumens per watt; the rest of the converted energy is wasted as heat.

Amount of Light	Incandescent Bulb	Fluorescent Bulb
900 lumens	60 watts	15 watts
1200 lumens	75 watts	20 watts
1750 lumens	100 watts	28 watts

Fluorescent bulbs
The gas in the tube glows with ultraviolet light when electricity from a magnetic or electronic ballast flows through it, making the bulb's phosphorus coating also glow. Fluorescent bulbs produce between 50 and 100 lumens per watt. They are three to four times more energy-efficient than incandescent bulbs and last about 10 times longer. Over time, the use of fluorescent bulbs can cost less than half as much as the use of incandescent bulbs.

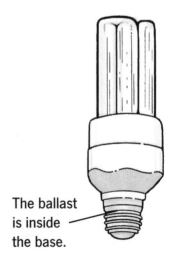

The ballast is inside the base.

Lighten Up

How can the energy needed to light your house be reduced?

Suggestions:

I = incandescent
F = fluorescent

Home Survey

Kind	Watts	# of bulbs	Total watts
	100 w		
	75 w		
	60 w		

Grand total		
Kilowatts		
Cost per hour		

All Fluorescents

Watts	# of bulbs	Total watts
28 w		
20 w		
15 w		

Grand total		
Kilowatts		
Cost per hour		

Cents

Cost per hour

Survey Fluores-cents
Light Bulbs

Your energy rate per kilowatt-hour:

1. What problems, if any, did you have getting the light bulb information? How can these problems be solved?

2. Which light bulb wattage was most common at your house? Which wattage was most common in all our houses?

3. Where do you need brighter lights? Where do you need dimmer lights?

4. How many light bulb watts are used in your house?

5. What is a kilowatt? How can we find our energy rate per kilowatt-hour?

6. If all the lights were on, how much would it cost per hour?

7. Which computations did you do mentally? ...on paper? ...with a calculator? Explain your choices.

8. In what ways can you save electricity?

9. What are you wondering now?

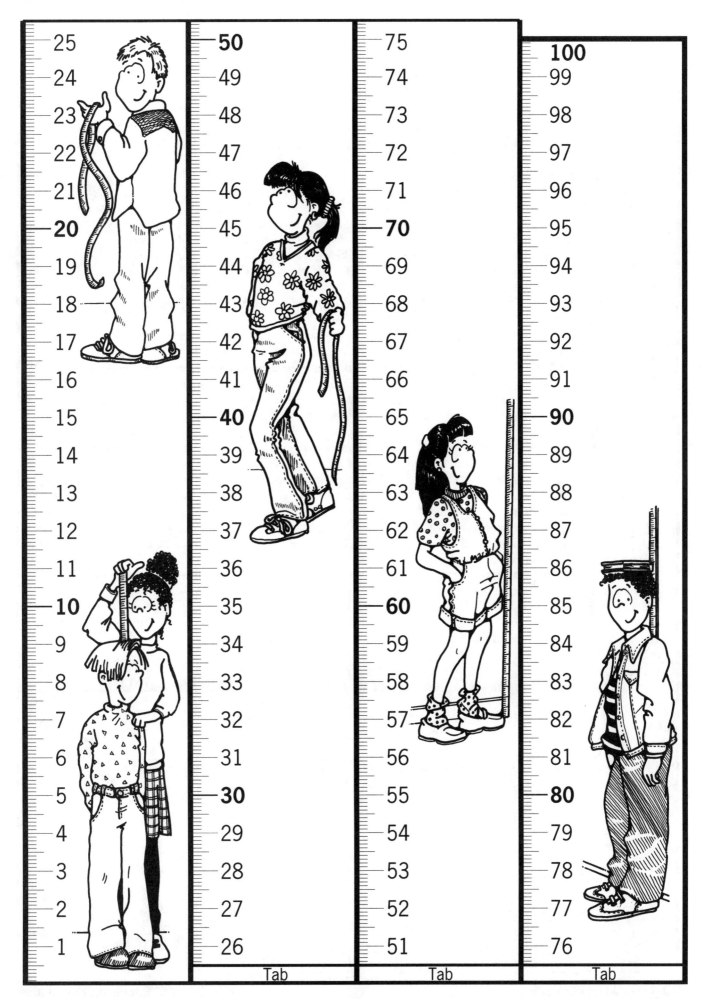

The AIMS Program

AIMS is the acronym for "**A**ctivities **I**ntegrating **M**athematics and **S**cience." Such integration enriches learning and makes it meaningful and holistic. AIMS began as a project of Fresno Pacific University to integrate the study of mathematics and science in grades K-9, but has since expanded to include language arts, social studies, and other disciplines.

AIMS is a continuing program of the non-profit AIMS Education Foundation. It had its inception in a National Science Foundation funded program whose purpose was to explore the effectiveness of integrating mathematics and science. The project directors in cooperation with 80 elementary classroom teachers devoted two years to a thorough field-testing of the results and implications of integration.

The approach met with such positive results that the decision was made to launch a program to create instructional materials incorporating this concept. Despite the fact that thoughtful educators have long recommended an integrative approach, very little appropriate material was available in 1981 when the project began. A series of writing projects have ensued, and today the AIMS Education Foundation is committed to continue the creation of new integrated activities on a permanent basis.

The AIMS program is funded through the sale of books, products, and staff development workshops and through proceeds from the Foundation's endowment. All net income from program and products flows into a trust fund administered by the AIMS Education Foundation. Use of these funds is restricted to support of research, development, and publication of new materials. Writers donate all their rights to the Foundation to support its on-going program. No royalties are paid to the writers.

The rationale for integration lies in the fact that science, mathematics, language arts, social studies, etc., are integrally interwoven in the real world from which it follows that they should be similarly treated in the classroom where we are preparing students to live in that world. Teachers who use the AIMS program give enthusiastic endorsement to the effectiveness of this approach.

Science encompasses the art of questioning, investigating, hypothesizing, discovering, and communicating. Mathematics is the language that provides clarity, objectivity, and understanding. The language arts provide us powerful tools of communication. Many of the major contemporary societal issues stem from advancements in science and must be studied in the context of the social sciences. Therefore, it is timely that all of us take seriously a more holistic mode of educating our students. This goal motivates all who are associated with the AIMS Program. We invite you to join us in this effort.

Meaningful integration of knowledge is a major recommendation coming from the nation's professional science and mathematics associations. The American Association for the Advancement of Science in *Science for All Americans* strongly recommends the integration of mathematics, science, and technology. The National Council of Teachers of Mathematics places strong emphasis on applications of mathematics such as are found in science investigations. AIMS is fully aligned with these recommendations.

Extensive field testing of AIMS investigations confirms these beneficial results:

1. Mathematics becomes more meaningful, hence more useful, when it is applied to situations that interest students.
2. The extent to which science is studied and understood is increased, with a significant economy of time, when mathematics and science are integrated.
3. There is improved quality of learning and retention, supporting the thesis that learning that is meaningful and relevant is more effective.
4. Motivation and involvement are increased dramatically as students investigate real-world situations and participate actively in the process.

We invite you to become part of this classroom teacher movement by using an integrated approach to learning and sharing any suggestions you may have.

The AIMS Program welcomes you!

AIMS Education Foundation Programs

Practical proven strategies to improve student achievement

When you host an AIMS workshop for elementary and middle school educators, you will know your teachers are receiving effective usable training they can apply in their classrooms immediately.

Designed for teachers—AIMS Workshops:

- Correlate to your state standards;
- Address key topic areas, including math content, science content, problem solving, and process skills;
- Teach you how to use AIMS' effective hands-on approach;
- Provide practice of activity-based teaching;
- Address classroom management issues, higher-order thinking skills, and materials;
- Give you AIMS resources; and
- Offer college (graduate-level) credits for many courses.

Aligned to district and administrator needs—AIMS workshops offer:

- Flexible scheduling and grade span options;
- Custom (one-, two-, or three-day) workshops to meet specific schedule, topic and grade-span needs;
- Pre-packaged one-day workshops on most major topics—only $3900 for up to 30 participants (includes all materials and expenses);
- Prepackaged four- or five-day workshops for in-depth math and science training—only $12,300 for up to 30 participants (includes all materials and expenses);
- Sustained staff development, by scheduling workshops throughout the school year and including follow-up and assessment;
- Eligibility for funding under the Title I and Title II sections of No Child Left Behind; and

- Affordable professional development—save when you schedule consecutive-day workshops.

University Credit—Correspondence Courses

AIMS offers correspondence courses through a partnership with Fresno Pacific University.

- Convenient distance-learning courses—you study at your own pace and schedule. No computer or Internet access required!

The tuition for each three-semester unit graduate-level course is $264 plus a materials fee.

The AIMS Instructional Leadership Program

This is an AIMS staff-development program seeking to prepare facilitators for leadership roles in science/math education in their home districts or regions. Upon successful completion of the program, trained facilitators become members of the AIMS Instructional Leadership Network, qualified to conduct AIMS workshops, teach AIMS in-service courses for college credit, and serve as AIMS consultants. Intensive training is provided in mathematics, science, process and thinking skills, workshop management, and other relevant topics.

Introducing AIMS Science Core Curriculum

Developed to meet 100% of your state's standards, AIMS' Science Core Curriculum gives students the opportunity to build content knowledge, thinking skills, and fundamental science processes.

- *Each* grade specific module has been developed to extend the AIMS approach to full-year science programs.
- *Each* standards-based module includes math, reading, hands-on investigations, and assessments.

Like all AIMS resources, these core modules are able to serve students at all stages of readiness, making these a great value across the grades served in your school.

For current information regarding the programs described above, please complete the following form and mail it to: P.O. Box 8120, Fresno, CA 93747.

Information Request

Please send current information on the items checked:

____ *Basic Information Packet* on AIMS materials ____ Hosting information for AIMS workshops
____ *AIMS Instructional Leadership Program* ____ AIMS Science Core Curriculum

Name _____ Phone _____

Address_____
          Street   City   State   Zip

© 2004 AIMS Education Foundation

AIMS Program Publications

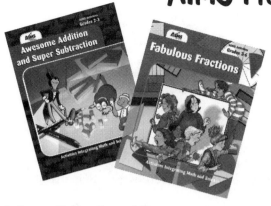

Actions with Fractions, 4-9
Awesome Addition and Super Subtraction, 2-3
Bats Incredible! 2-4
Brick Layers II, 4-9
Chemistry Matters, 4-7
Counting on Coins, K-2
Cycles of Knowing and Growing, 1-3
Crazy about Cotton, 3-7
Critters, 2-5
Electrical Connections, 4-9
Exploring Environments, K-6
Fabulous Fractions, 3-6
Fall into Math and Science, K-1
Field Detectives, 3-6
Finding Your Bearings, 4-9
Floaters and Sinkers, 5-9
From Head to Toe, 5-9
Fun with Foods, 5-9
Glide into Winter with Math and Science, K-1
Gravity Rules! 5-12
Hardhatting in a Geo-World, 3-5
It's About Time, K-2
It Must Be A Bird, Pre-K-2
Jaw Breakers and Heart Thumpers, 3-5
Looking at Geometry, 6-9
Looking at Lines, 6-9
Machine Shop, 5-9
Magnificent Microworld Adventures, 5-9
Marvelous Multiplication and Dazzling Division, 4-5
Math + Science, A Solution, 5-9
Mostly Magnets, 2-8
Movie Math Mania, 6-9
Multiplication the Algebra Way, 4-8
Off the Wall Science, 3-9
Out of This World, 4-8
Paper Square Geometry:
    The Mathematics of Origami, 5-12
Puzzle Play, 4-8
Pieces and Patterns, 5-9
Popping With Power, 3-5
Positive vs. Negative, 6-9
Primarily Bears, K-6
Primarily Earth, K-3

Primarily Physics, K-3
Primarily Plants, K-3
Problem Solving: Just for the Fun of It! 4-9
Problem Solving: Just for the Fun of It! Book Two, 4-9
Proportional Reasoning, 6-9
Ray's Reflections, 4-8
Sense-Able Science, K-1
Soap Films and Bubbles, 4-9
Solve It! K-1: Problem-Solving Strategies, K-1
Solve It! 2nd: Problem-Solving Strategies, 2
Solve It! 3rd: Problem-Solving Strategies, 3
Spatial Visualization, 4-9
Spills and Ripples, 5-12
Spring into Math and Science, K-1
The Amazing Circle, 4-9
The Budding Botanist, 3-6
The Sky's the Limit, 5-9
Through the Eyes of the Explorers, 5-9
Under Construction, K-2
Water Precious Water, 2-6
Weather Sense: Temperature, Air Pressure, and Wind, 4-5
Weather Sense: Moisture, 4-5
Winter Wonders, K-2

Spanish Supplements*
Fall Into Math and Science, K-1
Glide Into Winter with Math and Science, K-1
Mostly Magnets, 2-8
Pieces and Patterns, 5-9
Primarily Bears, K-6
Primarily Physics, K-3
Sense-Able Science, K-1
Spring Into Math and Science, K-1

* Spanish supplements are only available as downloads from the
AIMS website. The supplements contain only the student pages
in Spanish; you will need the English version of the book for the
teacher's text.

Spanish Edition
Constructores II: Ingeniería Creativa Con Construcciones
    LEGO® 4-9
    The entire book is written in Spanish. English pages not included.

Other Science and Math Publications
Historical Connections in Mathematics, Vol. I, 5-9
Historical Connections in Mathematics, Vol. II, 5-9
Historical Connections in Mathematics, Vol. III, 5-9
Mathematicians are People, Too
Mathematicians are People, Too, Vol. II
What's Next, Volume 1, 4-12
What's Next, Volume 2, 4-12
What's Next, Volume 3, 4-12

For further information write to:
AIMS Education Foundation • P.O. Box 8120 • Fresno, California 93747-8120
www.aimsedu.org • 559.255.6396 (fax) • 888.733.2467 (toll free)

Duplication Rights

Standard Duplication Rights

Purchasers of AIMS activities (individually or in books and magazines) may make up to 200 copies of any portion of the purchased activities, provided these copies will be used for educational purposes and only at one school site.

Workshop or conference presenters may make one copy of a purchased activity for each participant, with a limit of five activities per workshop or conference session.

Standard duplication rights apply to activities received at workshops, free sample activities provided by AIMS, and activities received by conference participants.

All copies must bear the AIMS Education Foundation copyright information.

Unlimited Duplication Rights

To ensure compliance with copyright regulations, AIMS users may upgrade from standard to unlimited duplication rights. Such rights permit unlimited duplication of purchased activities (including revisions) for use at a given school site.

Activities received at workshops are eligible for upgrade from standard to unlimited duplication rights.

Free sample activities and activities received as a conference participant are not eligible for upgrade from standard to unlimited duplication rights.

Upgrade Fees

The fees for upgrading from standard to unlimited duplication rights are:
* $5 per activity per site,
* $25 per book per site, and
* $10 per magazine issue per site.

The cost of upgrading is shown in the following examples:
* activity: 5 activities x 5 sites x $5 = $125
* book: 10 books x 5 sites x $25 = $1250
* magazine issue: 1 issue x 5 sites x $10 = $50

Purchasing Unlimited Duplication Rights

To purchase unlimited duplication rights, please provide us the following:
1. The name of the individual responsible for coordinating the purchase of duplication rights.
2. The title of each book, activity, and magazine issue to be covered.
3. The number of school sites and name of each site for which rights are being purchased.
4. Payment (check, purchase order, credit card)

Requested duplication rights are automatically authorized with payment. The individual responsible for coordinating the purchase of duplication rights will be sent a certificate verifying the purchase.

Internet Use

Permission to make AIMS activities available on the Internet is determined on a case-by-case basis.

* P. O. Box 8120, Fresno, CA 93747-8120 *
* permissions@aimsedu.org * www.aimsedu.org *
* 559.255.6396 (fax) * 888.733.2467 (toll free) *